HOUGHTON MIFFLIN

California Science

Interactive Text

HOUGHTON MIFFLIN   BOSTON

Printed in the U.S.A.

ISBN 13: 978-0-547-00463-1
ISBN 10: 0-547-00463-X

15 16 17   0877   18 17 16

4500612773

Contents

Adaptations to Land and Water 2

When Environments Change 22

Organisms of Long Ago 42

Our Solar System 62

Cycles and Patterns in Space 88

Properties of Matter 116

Chemical Changes 144

Forms of Energy 164

Light 184

Index 204

Credits 211

WHAT DO YOU KNOW?

a. Give an example of a living thing that is adapted to living on land. Then tell what adaptation it has.

_____

_____

_____

b. Give an example of a living thing that is adapted to living in water. Then tell what adaptation is has.

_____

_____

_____

Adaptations to Land and Water

Contents

1 What Organisms Live in Forests
and Grasslands? 4

2 What Organisms Live in Tundra
and Deserts? 8

3 What Organisms Live in
Water Habitats? 13

Glossary 18

WHAT DO YOU WANT TO KNOW?

Read the lesson titles in the contents list. Write a question you have about how plants and animals are adapted to live in one of the habitats.

_____

_____

_____

Skim the pictures and headings in this chapter. Write another question that you have about how plants and animals are adapted to live in another one of the habitats.

_____

_____

_____

VOCABULARY

adaptation A way of acting or a body part that helps a living thing survive. *(noun)*

behavior The way that an organism usually acts in a certain situation. *(noun)*

biome A large area that has similar living things and about the same temperature and rainfall throughout. *(noun)*

forest A large area in which there are many trees growing close together. *(noun)*

grassland An area made up of large, flat land that is covered with grasses. *(noun)*

habitat The place where a plant or an animal lives. *(noun)*

3.a. Students know plants and animals have parts that help them grow, survive, and reproduce.
3.b. Students know examples of different kinds of organisms that live in oceans, deserts, tundra, forests, grasslands, and wetlands.

1 What Organisms Live in Forests and Grasslands?

Forests and grasslands are different places with different living things. The living things have changed over time so that they can live there.

Living in the Forest

A **forest** (FAWR ihst) is a large area, or piece of land. It has many trees. Many plants and animals live in a forest biome (BY ohm). A **biome** is a large area that has the same living things and weather across the whole area.

Living things are called organisms. The organisms that live in a forest have adaptations (ad dap TAY shuhnz) that help them live there. An **adaptation** is a way of acting or a body part that helps a living thing to live.

Some forest trees grow very tall. This is an adaptation that helps their leaves get sunlight, or light from the Sun.

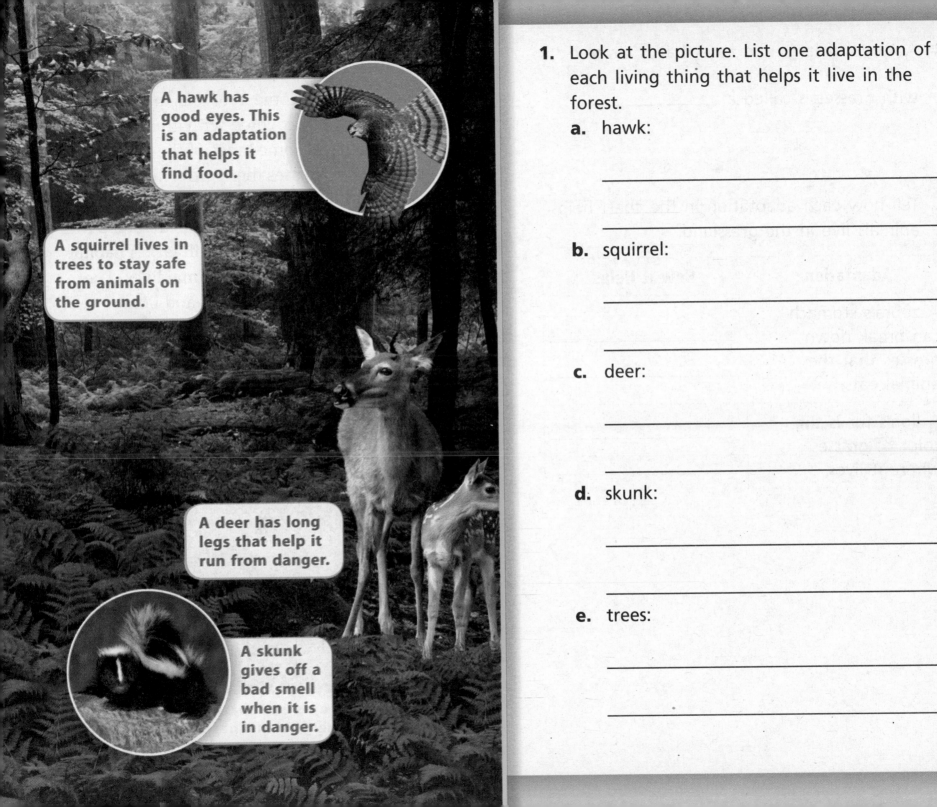

A hawk has good eyes. This is an adaptation that helps it find food.

A squirrel lives in trees to stay safe from animals on the ground.

A deer has long legs that help it run from danger.

A skunk gives off a bad smell when it is in danger.

1. Look at the picture. List one adaptation of each living thing that helps it live in the forest.

a. hawk:

_____

_____

b. squirrel:

_____

_____

c. deer:

_____

_____

d. skunk:

_____

_____

e. trees:

_____

_____

5

2. An area of large flat land that is covered

with grasses is called a _____.

3. Tell how each adaptation in the chart helps animals live in the grassland.

Adaptation	How It Helps
A zebra's stomach can break down grasses that the animal eats.	_____ _____ _____
A lion's fur is the color of grasses where it lives.	_____ _____

Grassland Survival

A **grassland** is a biome, too. It is an area of large, flat land. It is covered with grasses. The grassland is dry at some times of the year. When it does rain, the grasses there grow fast.

Zebras and lions are animals that live in grasslands. They have adaptations that help them live in their habitat (HAB ih tat). A **habitat** is the place where a plant or animal lives. The grassland is a habitat for zebras and lions.

A zebra's stomach helps it break down grasses that it eats. This is an adaptation.

A lion has good eyes and sharp claws. A lion's fur is the color of the grasses. These are adaptations.

Types of Adaptations

Some adaptations are structural adaptations. A structural adaptation is a body part that helps a plant or animal live. A cat has strong back legs. It uses the legs to jump on a mouse. This is a structural adaptation.

Some adaptations are behaviors. A **behavior** is the way a living thing acts. A cat walks up to a mouse very quietly. This adaptation is a behavior.

cat

mouse

The cat has both behaviors and structural adaptations that help it catch the mouse.

CLASSIFY

What are two kinds of adaptations?

Summary Organisms have adaptations that help them live in the forests and grasslands. Some adapations are structural. Other adapations are the way a living thing acts. These adaptations are behaviors.

Describe adaptations of a cat.

a. structural:

_____

_____

b. behavior:

_____

_____

Classify What are two kinds of adaptations?

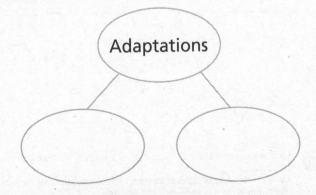

Adaptations

VOCABULARY

desert An area that receives less than about 25 cm (10 in.) of precipitation in a year. *(noun)*

environment All the living and nonliving things that surround and affect an organism. *(noun)*

tundra A cold, treeless area that has short, cool summers and long, cold winters. *(noun)*

VOCABULARY SKILL: Homographs

Homographs are words that are spelled the same way but have different meanings. They may also be pronounced differently.

Read the definition of the word *desert* (DEHZ urt) above. The homograph *desert* (dih ZURT) means "to leave empty or alone." Make a drawing to show the meaning of the vocabulary term *desert*.

3.a. Students know plants and animals have parts that help them grow, survive, and reproduce.
3.b. Students know examples of different kinds of organisms that live in oceans, deserts, tundra, forests, grasslands, and wetlands.

2 What Organisms Live in Tundra and Deserts?

The tundra and the desert are very different biomes. They both have living things with adaptations that help them live there.

Surviving on the Tundra

The **tundra** (TUHN drah) is a very cold area without trees. The summers are short and cool. The winters are long and cold. Snow covers the ground for most of the year. It is hard for many things to live in the tundra.

The tundra is an **environment** (ehn VY ruhn muhnt). An environment is everything around an organism. It has living things, such as plants and animals. It also has nonliving things, such as air and water.

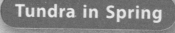

Tundra in Spring

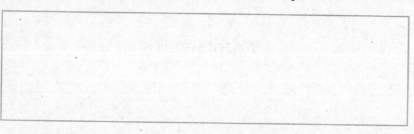

Tundra plants are short so that they can stay safe from wind.

This bird changes color to match the things around it.

Most plants in the tundra grow close to the ground. This keeps them safe from strong winds that blow there. The plants grow very fast, too. The tundra only has a few warm months each year. The plants do not have much time to grow. These are adaptations that help plants live in the tundra.

Some tundra animals can change color! Their coat turns from brown to white in winter to help them hide in the snow. They have thick fur and a lot of fat to help them stay warm. Some animals rest all winter to stay out of the cold. These are adaptations that help animals live in the tundra.

1. (Circle) the words that correctly describe plant and animal adaptations to the tundra.

Tundra Plants	Tundra Animals
a. grow close to the (river, ground)	**a.** may change (color, habitat)
b. grow (fast, slow)	**b.** have (thick, thin) fur
c. grow (tall, short)	**c.** have (little, a lot of) fat

2. A desert is an area that gets very

_____.

3. Animals that live in the desert need

adaptations that help them _____

water and _____ water.

4. What behavior of a desert squirrel is an adaptation that helps it to keep cool?

_____

Surviving in the Desert

A **desert** is an area that gets little rain. It is very hot. Many organisms in the desert have adaptations that help them find and keep water.

Snakes and lizards have hard skin that holds in water. This is a structural adaptation that helps them live in the desert.

Squirrels live in the ground where it is not as hot. This is a behavior that helps squirrels stay cool.

Desert

squirrel

Most desert plants have roots that can take in a lot of water very fast. Cactuses have thick stems that hold water for the dry months.

Some plants wait for rain and then grow very fast. These are adaptations that help them live in the desert.

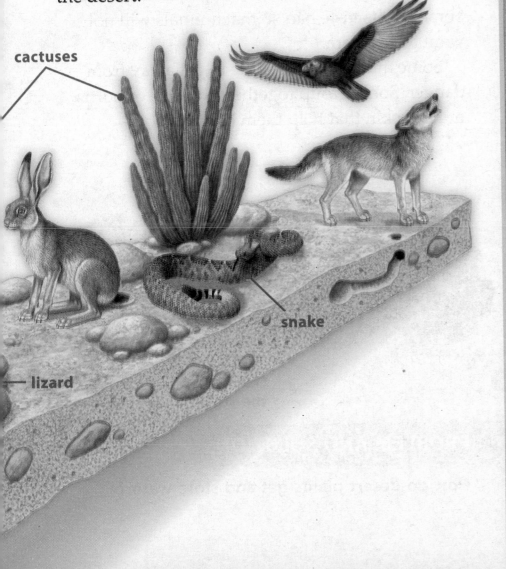

cactuses

snake

lizard

5. (Circle) the animals that are adapted to the desert.

6. Describe the adaptations that help a rattlesnake live in the desert.
   a. structural:

   _____

   b. behavior:

   _____

   _____

7. (Circle) the words in the chart that correctly describe plant and animal adaptations to the desert.

Desert Plants	Desert Animals
a. have (thick, thin) stems	a. have (hard, soft) skin
b. grow (fast, slow)	b. live in (trees, in the ground)
c. have roots that take in water (quickly, slowly).	

Summary The tundra and the desert are two extreme environments. Organisms in these biomes have adaptations that help them survive.

What are some self-defense adaptations that keep organisms safe in their habitat?

a. plants:

_____

_____

b. animals:

_____

_____

Problem and Solution How do desert plants get and store water?

Problem	Solution
Desert plants must get and store water.	

Self-Defense

Organisms in every habitat have adaptations that help them stay safe. This is called self-defense.

Desert plants have to stay safe from animals that want to get water from them. Some plants have spines, or points, that keep animals away. Some plants taste bad so that animals will not want to eat them.

Some animals run or hide to get away from danger. Some group together. Some have horns or hard skin that help them fight back.

Oxen stand in a circle to keep the young oxen safe.

PROBLEM AND SOLUTION

How do desert plants get and store water?

What Organisms Live in Water Habitats? ③

Many habitats are under water. The organisms in these habitats adapt to living in water.

Life in a Tide Pool

Tide pools are pools of water left behind when water flows back out to sea. A tide pool is an aquatic (uh KWAT ihk) habitat. An **aquatic habitat** is a place where organisms live in or around water.

Plants and animals in a tide pool have adaptations that help them live in the salty water. Adaptations help them eat, grow, and stay safe.

Adaptations to Tide Pools

This grass lets off salt from its leaves so that it can live in salt water.

This snail goes in its shell to hide.

This crab uses its strong claws to catch and eat snails.

VOCABULARY

aquatic habitat A place where organisms live in or on water. *(noun)*

VOCABULARY SKILL: Break It Apart

You will be learning about wetland habitats in this lesson. The word *wetland* is made of two words: *wet* and *land*. From these two words, guess what a wetland is.

_____

_____

 3.a. Students know plants and animals have parts that help them grow, survive, and reproduce.
3.b. Students know examples of different kinds of organisms that live in oceans, deserts, tundra, forests, grasslands, and wetlands.

1. (Circle) the tide pool organisms.

2. How do the long legs of a sea bird keep the bird dry?

_____

_____

3. Both a blue crab and a squirrel have claws. How does each animal use its claws to live in its habitat? (Look back at the squirrel on page 5 if you need help.)

Blue Crabs   Squirrels

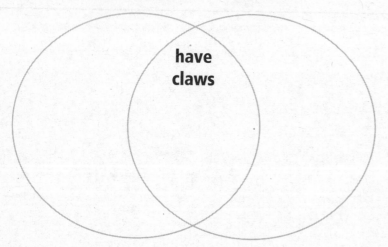

have
claws

Some animals can close their shell. It keeps water in with them when the tide pool dries up. Sea birds have long legs that help them walk in water. These are structural adaptations.

Long legs help this bird walk in water.

Life in the Ocean

An ocean is another aquatic habitat. From land, the ocean may look like it does not have many plants and animals. But the ocean has many living things.

The top of the ocean is called the surface. Near the surface, the water is warm and there is a lot of sunlight. Many plants and animals live there.

As you go down in the ocean, there is less light. The water is not as warm. There are no plants, but there are many animals.

As you get very deep in the ocean, there is no light. Some animals have body parts that light up to help them find food.

These plants grow near the surface of the ocean where they can get sunlight.

I Wonder . . . Plants live only near the surface of the ocean. Why do you think this is so?

_____

_____

_____

4. Draw and label an animal that lives at each level of the ocean.

Surface

Middle

Deep

Dolphins have holes on the top of their heads to help them get air.

An octopus can change color to match the things around it.

This fish has lights on its body that help it find food.

Wetlands

A wetland is another aquatic habitat. The ground in a wetland is covered with a small amount of water. Organisms have adaptations that help them live there.

Wetland birds have long legs so that they can walk in water. Their mouths help them catch fish.

Plants have adaptations that help them live in water, too. Trees have strong roots that hold them up. The roots can be in salt water.

big mouth

strong roots

COMPARE AND CONTRAST

How are a tide pool and the deep ocean alike and different?

Summary   Many habitiats are partly or completely under water. The organisms in these habitats have adapted to living in water. What adaptations do organisms have that help them live in wetlands?

a. birds:

_____

b. plants:

_____

Compare and Contrast   How are a tide pool and the deep ocean alike and different?

Tide Pool   Deep Ocean

Write a sentence using as many vocabulary terms from this page as possible.

_____

_____

_____

adaptation (ad dap TAY shun) A way of acting or a body part that helps a living thing survive.

adaptación Forma de actuar de un ser vivo; parte del cuerpo que le ayuda a sobrevivir.

aquatic habitat (uh KWAT ihk HAB ih tat) A place where organisms live in or on water.

hábitat acuático Lugar donde los organismos viven dentro o cerca del agua.

behavior (bee HAYV yur) The way that an organism usually acts in a certain situation.

comportamiento Forma en la que usualmente actúa un organismo en una situación determinada.

biome (BY ohm) A large area that has similar living things and about the same temperature and rainfall throughout.

bioma Zona extensa que tiene similares seres vivos, temperaturas y lluvias.

desert (DEHZ urt) An area that receives less than about 25 cm (10 in.) of precipitation in a year.

desierto Zona que recibe menos de unos 25 cm (10 pulg.) de precipitación al año.

Glossary

environment (ehn VY ruhn muhnt) All the living and nonliving things that surround and affect an organism.

medio ambiente Todos los seres vivos y las cosas sin vida que rodean y afectan a un organismo.

forest (FAWR ihst) A large area in which there are many trees growing close together.

bosque Zona grande donde muchos árboles crecen juntos.

grassland (GRAS land) An area made up of large, flat land that is covered with grasses.

pastizal Zona formada por terrenos grandes y llanos, cubiertos de hierbas.

habitat (HAB ih tat) The place where a plant or animal lives.

hábitat Lugar donde vive una planta o animal.

tundra (TUHN drah) A cold, treeless area that has short, cool summers and long, cold winters.

tundra Zona fría sin árboles donde los veranos son cortos y frescos y los inviernos largos y fríos.

 Visit www.eduplace.com to play puzzles and word games.

(Circle) the words that are the same in both English and Spanish.

Chapter Review

K W L

WHAT DID YOU LEARN?

❶ Circle the correct answer.

❷ _____

_____

❸ _____

_____

❹ _____

_____

❺ _____

_____

_____

_____

20

Think About What You Have Read

Vocabulary

❶ A behavior or body part that helps a living thing live in its environment is a/an _____.

A) biome

B) adaptation

C) tundra

D) habitat

Comprehension

❷ Describe a forest.

❸ What are two ways that animals defend themselves?

❹ Compare an adaptation of an animal that lives in an aquatic habitat to one that lives on land.

Critical Thinking

❺ Use what you know about the adaptations of tundra plants to explain why there are no trees in the tundra.

WHAT DO YOU KNOW?

List one fact about each of these topics:

a. How living things compete _____

_____

_____

_____

b. How living things change environments

_____

_____

_____

When Environments Change

Contents

1 How Do Living Things Compete? . . . 24

2 How Do Living Things Change
   Environments? 30

Glossary 38

WHAT DO YOU WANT TO KNOW?

Skim the pictures and headings in this chapter. List three things that you want to find out about living things and their environments.

a. _____

_____

_____

b. _____

_____

_____

c. _____

_____

_____

VOCABULARY

community A group of organisms that live in the same area and interact with one another. *(noun)*

competition The struggle of one organism against another to gain resources. *(noun)*

ecosystem All the living and nonliving things that exist and interact in one place. *(noun)*

population All the living organisms of the same kind that live in an area. *(noun)*

reproduce To make new living things of the same kind. *(verb)*

resource A thing found in nature that is useful to organisms. *(noun)*

VOCABULARY SKILL: Prefix and Suffix

The prefix *re-* means "again." *Produce* means "to make." Write the meaning of *reproduce*.

_____

_____

3.c. Students know living things cause changes in their environment; some changes harm and some help the organism or other organisms.
3.d. Students know when the environment changes, some plants and animals live and reproduce; others die or move away.

24

1 How Do Living Things Compete?

There is not enough food, water, or space for all of the living things in an environment. Organisms must work to get these things, and this changes the environment.

Competing for Food and Water

All the snakes that live in a grassland make up a population (pahp yuh LAY shuhn). A **population** is all the organisms of the same kind that live in an area.

The snakes and all of the other animals in the grassland make up a community (kuh MYOO-nih tee). A **community** is a group of organisms that live in the same area and interact with one another. All the populations in an area make up the community.

snake

coyote

skunk

Snakes, coyotes, and skunks are part of a grassland community. Each kind of animal is also its own population.

above surface

POND ECOSYSTEM
Water lilies need space to grow and sunlight to make food. Sunlight and space are resources.

water lilies

below surface

An **ecosystem** (EE koh SIHS tuhm) is all the living and nonliving things in one place. All of the living things need to get enough resources (REE sawrs ehz) to live. A **resource** is a thing found in nature that organisms can use.

Food and water are resources. Air and a safe place to live are resources, too. All living things need them.

1. All the organisms of the same kind that live in an area are a _____.

2. A group of organisms that live in the same area and interact with each other is a

_____.

3. Circle the picture that best shows a population of water lilies.

4. Look at the pictures on this page. List two resources that water lilies use in the pond ecosystem.

   a. _____

   b. _____

5. Explain what the word *competition* means.

_____

_____

_____

6. Look at the picture. How are the bird and squirrel competing?

_____

_____

7. Circle the sentence that tells what is likely to happen to an organism if it does not get all the resources it needs.

- The organism is likely to grow bigger.

- The organism is likely to die.

- The organism is likely to remain unchanged.

26

Often there is not enough of a resource for all the organisms that need it. Organisms are in competition (kom pih TISH uhn) for that resource. **Competition** is two organisms trying to get the same resource.

Competition can change the environment. If an organism does not get all of the resources it needs, it will die.

The bird and the squirrel are in competition for food.

Sea lions compete for space.

Competing for Space

Living things need space to live and reproduce (ree proh DOOS). To **reproduce** is to make new living things of the same kind.

Birds need space on tree branches to build nests. Trees need space for their roots to grow.

8. Why do birds and trees need space?

   a. birds: _____

   _____

   b. trees: _____

   _____

9. To make new living things of the same kind

   is to _____.

10. Complete the sentences to tell how moose compete for resources.

Moose are big animals. Moose need a lot

of _____. Sometimes humans build houses in areas where moose live. Then the

moose no longer have enough _____

to meet their _____.

11. Tell the size of each population. Use the words *large* and *small*.

a. many horses in a field = _____ population size

b. few horses in a field = _____ population size

12. Explain how the amount of resources can affect population size.

_____

_____

_____

moose

people

Moose are big animals. They need a lot of space. Sometimes people build homes in areas where moose live. Then the moose do not have enough space to meet their needs. They may go to places where people live. That can be dangerous for the moose and for the people.

People need space, too. Have you ever been on a bus with a lot of people? You competed for space when you tried to find a place to sit.

Resources and Population Size

Population size is the number of one kind of living thing in an area. If there are a lot of horses in a field, the population size is large. If there are only a few horses, the population is small.

Population size is based on the number of resources in an area. If living things do not get the things they need, they may die. If many of them die, the population size goes down.

If there are too many horses in an area, they will not all get what they need to live. The horses will compete for food and space. Then the horse population size will go down.

MAIN IDEA

What are two resources for which living things compete?

Summary Changes in the environment are caused by living and nonliving things. Look at the picture of the horses. What might happen if there are too many horses in an area?

_____

_____

_____

_____

Main Idea What are two resources for which living things compete?

Living things compete for . . .

_____   _____

29

VOCABULARY

drought A long time with little to no rainfall. *(noun)*

pollution The addition of any harmful materials to the environment. *(noun)*

VOCABULARY SKILL: Decode Words

Write the word *drought*. Circle the blend that begins this word (*dr*). In this word, the letters *-ought* make the same sound as *o-u-t* in the word *out*. Write the word *drought* the way it sounds. Practice saying the word.

3.c. Students know living things cause changes in their environment; some changes harm and some help the organism or other organisms.
3.d. Students know when the environment changes, some plants and animals live and reproduce; others die or move away.

2 How Do Living Things Change Environments?

Living and nonliving things change the environment. The changes can help or hurt things in the environment.

Fire

A forest fire can hurt many of the living things in the forest. Fire can kill small plants. The plants were food for many animals. When the plants are gone, the animals have to find new food.

Fire can kill trees and big plants, too. The trees were home for many animals. When the trees are gone, the animals have to find a new place to live.

A forest fire can help the living things in the forest, too.

A fire cleans up the forest floor. That can make new places for animals to live.

The fire leaves a lot of nutrients, or things that plants need. New plants can grow. The new plants are food for animals.

Some organisms adapt to the changes. Some do not. The organisms that adapt are the ones that live.

> These pine trees have adaptations that help them in a fire. They hold on to their seeds until after the fire. Then the seeds grow into new plants.

1. Complete the chart about forest fires.

Forest Fires	
Cause	**Effect**
Plants are destroyed.	Some animals will lose _____ or _____.
Fire cleans up the forest floor.	There is more _____ for new plants and animals.
Fires leave _____.	New plants can grow.
Seeds are released.	New plants will _____.

I Wonder . . . Are all the effects of a forest fire harmful? What do you think?

_____

_____

_____

_____

2. Look at the picture of the flood. Tell one harmful thing and one helpful thing that happens to living things because of a flood.

a. harmful: _____

_____.

b. helpful: _____

_____.

Flood and Drought

A flood happens when water from rivers and lakes covers the land. After a flood, many people and animals do not have a home to go back to. Plants die as water covers them and blocks sunlight.

A flood can help living things, too. When the water dries up, it leaves a lot of nutrients that help plants grow. New plants can grow where they could not grow before the flood.

Floods can help and hurt the environment.

Droughts can help and hurt the environment.

A **drought** is a long time with little or no rain. Many plants die in a drought because they do not get enough water. Animals that eat those plants have to move to a new area to find food.

A drought can help living things, too. Organisms that eat dead plants and animals can find a lot of food after a drought.

3. What is a drought?

_____

_____

4. Fill in the diagram to tell what happens during a drought.

Drought

_____
_____

_____
_____

_____
_____

33

5. List two harmful changes that a new tree can bring.

a. _____

_____

b. _____

_____

I Wonder . . . A gardener plants a vine that came from an ecosystem in another country. What harm could the vine do?

_____

_____

_____

_____

Plants Cause Change

Plants change the environment around them. A tree growing in an open area changes the things around it. Trees make shade. They take nutrients from the ground. Grasses and small plants that do not get enough sunlight or nutrients may die. Other plants and animals that could not live in the area now have a place to live.

People have moved some plants from one ecosystem to another. The new plants can grow fast in the new area. They make a lot of changes in the new environment.

This plant is called kudzu. It is from Japan. It grows so fast that it can cover trees, signs, and houses!

Animals Cause Change

Animals can change the environment, too. Animals that eat grass can eat the tops off of a population of grasses. Big animals push plants down.

Animals moving from place to place can carry seeds in their fur. The seeds fall off and grow in the new area where they did not grow before.

Beavers change the environment.

6. Complete the chart:

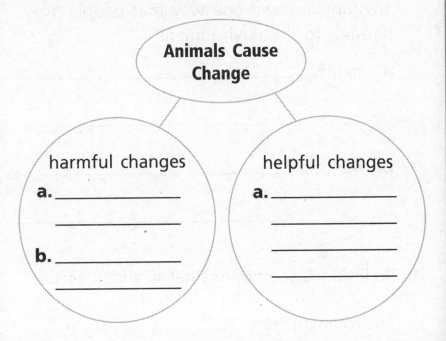

Animals Cause Change

harmful changes

a._____

_____

b._____

_____

helpful changes

a._____

_____

_____

_____

7. Look at the picture on this page. The beavers are building a dam across a stream. What might happen to the area downstream when the dam is complete?

_____

_____

_____

8. List one way that people are helpful to the environment and one way that people are harmful to the environment.

   a. helpful: _____

   _____

   b. harmful: _____

   _____

9. Pollution is something that is added to the

   environment that _____ it.

10. List three kinds of pollution.

Pollution

   a. _____

   b. _____

   c. _____

Pollution

People can help and hurt the environment, too. People build houses and roads. They build farms and cities. The things people build take away homes for plants and animals.

Things people do can make pollution (puh-LOO shuhn). **Pollution** is something that is added to the environment that hurts it.

People leave things that they do not need on the ground. They pour waste into rivers and lakes. They make smoke that fills the air. These are all kinds of pollution.

Pollution can kill animals and plants. It can take away their homes. It can change the environment for many years.

Pollution can kill plants and animals.

People can help the environment by putting trash where it belongs.

People can help the environment, too. People make laws that keep the environment safe. Laws can limit hunting and fishing. Laws can keep animal homes safe from building and pollution.

CAUSE AND EFFECT

In what ways do people protect the environment?

Summary Changes to the environment are caused by living and nonliving things. These changes can be harmful and helpful. Look at the picture. How have people hurt the environment? How can the boy help?

_____

_____

Cause and Effect List something people can do to protect the environment.

Cause	Effect
_____ _____ _____ _____	People help the environment.

Group two or more of the words on the page and explain why they go together.

community (kuh MYOO nih tee) A group of organisms that live in the same area and interact with one another.

comunidad Grupo de organismos que viven en la misma zona e interactúan unos con otros.

competition (kom pih TISH uhn) The struggle of one organism against another to gain resources.

competencia Lucha de un organismo contra otro para obtener recursos.

drought (drowt) A long time with little to no rainfall.

sequía Período largo de tiempo durante el cual no llueve nada o llueve poco.

ecosystem (EE koh SIHS tehm) All the living and nonliving things that exist and interact in one place.

ecosistema Todos los seres vivos y las cosas sin vida que existen e interactúan en un lugar.

Glossary

pollution (puh LOO shuhn) The addition of any harmful materials to the environment.

contaminación Liberación de sustancias perjudiciales para el medio ambiente.

population (pahp yuh LAY shuhn) All the living organisms of the same kind that live in an area.

población Todos los organismos vivos del mismo tipo que viven en una zona.

reproduce (ree proh DOOS) To make new living things of the same kind.

reproducir Crear nuevos seres vivos del mismo tipo.

resource (REE sawrs) A thing found in nature that is useful to organisms.

recurso Objeto que se encuentra en la naturaleza y es útil para los organismos.

 Visit www.eduplace.com to play puzzles and word games.

Circle the English words and their meanings for all the glossary words.

Chapter Review

WHAT DID YOU LEARN?

Vocabulary

❶ Circle the correct answer.

Comprehension

❷ _____

_____

❸ _____

_____

❹ _____

_____

Critical Thinking

❺ _____

_____

Responding

Think About What You Have Read

Vocabulary

❶ The struggle between organisms for resources is called _____.

   A) community

   B) competition

   C) drought

   D) population

Comprehension

❷ What must organisms compete for?

❸ What can cause changes to an environment?

❹ What is pollution?

Critical Thinking

❺ Two bears compete for fish. One bear can swim. The other bear is hurt and cannot swim. Which bear is more likely to live? Why?

WHAT DO YOU KNOW?

List one fact about each of these topics:

a. What threatens the survival of species

_____

_____

_____

b. What we can learn from fossils

_____

_____

_____

c. How extinct and living things are alike

_____

_____

_____

Organisms of Long Ago

Contents

1 What Threatens the Survival
of Species? 44

2 What Can Be Learned from Fossils? . . . 49

3 How Are Extinct and Living
Things Alike? 53

Glossary 58

WHAT DO YOU WANT TO KNOW?

Skim the pictures and headings in this chapter. List one thing you want to find out about each of these topics:

a. How scientists learn about living things from long ago

_____

_____

_____

b. Living things from long ago

_____

_____

_____

VOCABULARY

endangered species A species that has so few members that the entire species is at risk of dying out. *(noun)*

extinct species A species that has died off. *(noun)*

species A group of the same type of living thing that can mate and produce other living things of the same kind. *(noun)*

VOCABULARY SKILL: Prefixes

In the word *endangered,* the prefix *en-* means "to put into." Think about the meaning of the word *danger.* Now put the two word parts together. What does that tell you about the meaning of the term *endangered species*?

_____

_____

_____

3.d. Students know when the environment changes, some plants and animals live and reproduce; others die or move away.
3.e. Students know that some kinds of organisms that once lived on Earth have completely disappeared; some of those organisms resembled organisms that are alive today.

44

1 What Threatens the Survival of Species?

A kind of organism that once lived on Earth but does not now is extinct. A kind of organism that is almost extinct is called endangered.

Natural Threats

Dinosaurs were animals that lived many years ago. There were many species (SPEE sheez) of dinosaur. A **species** is a group of the same kind of living thing that can produce living things of the same kind.

Dinosaurs are extinct.

All of the different species of dinosaur became extinct (ihk STIHNGKT) long ago. An **extinct species** is one that has died off.

Dinosaurs probably became extinct when a large rock from space hit Earth. Then Earth became dark and cold. Dinosaurs are extinct because they could not live after their environment changed.

Organisms that live now can become extinct, too. Volcanoes and fires can kill many living things and take away their homes. Acts of nature can lead to species becoming extinct.

This species of sea turtle is almost extinct. In 2004, there was a tsunami, or giant wave. It killed many of the turtles.

This sea turtle may soon be extinct.

1. Complete the diagram to show how dinosaurs became extinct.

A large _____ from space hit _____.

↓

Earth became _____ and _____.

↓

Dinosaurs could not live because their _____ changed.

↓

Dinosaurs became extinct.

2. What is one way that people cause species to become extinct?

_____

_____

_____

3. Fill in the timeline to show how the bison population has changed.

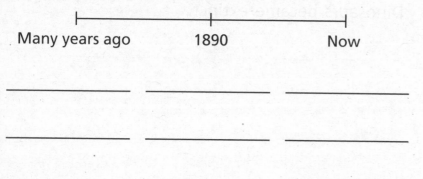

Many years ago   1890   Now

_____   _____   _____

_____   _____   _____

_____   _____   _____

Human Threats

People lead to species becoming extinct, too. People hunt animals. If they hunt too many of one species, it can become extinct.

This animal is a bison (BY suhn). There were a lot of bison many years ago. Then people hunted them. In 1890 there were only 750 bison left. Now people are helping the bison population to get big again. There are about half a million bison today!

bison

dodo bird

People build homes and roads. They cut down forests and change the places where animals live. These changes take away resources that species need to live, so some of them may become extinct.

If people bring new species into an area, species already in that area may become extinct. The dodo was a bird that could not fly. People moved to where dodos lived. They brought pigs, rats, and dogs with them. Those animals ate the dodos and their eggs. Also, people hunted the dodos. Now the dodos are extinct.

4. A bird makes its home in a pine tree. Builders cut down all the pine trees in an area to make room for new houses. What might happen to the bird?

_____

_____

_____

5. Circle the sentences that tell why dodos became extinct.

People hunted dodos.

A large volcano killed the dodos.

New species of animals came to where the dodos lived.

A big storm destroyed the dodos' homes.

Summary People can cause living things to become endangered or extinct. Tell what an endangered species is.

_____

_____

_____

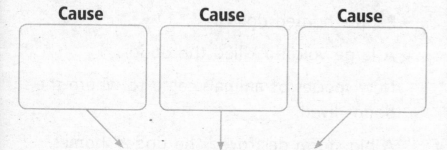

Cause and Effect What can cause a species to become endangered or extinct?

Cause	Cause	Cause

Effect

A species becomes endangered or extinct.

Endangered Species

Species that are close to becoming extinct are called endangered species (ehn DAYN jurd SPEE sheez). An **endangered species** is one that has so few living things that the whole species may die off.

This sheep is an endangered species.

CAUSE AND EFFECT

What can cause a species to become endangered or extinct?

What Can Be Learned from Fossils?

2

Parts of once-living things can be saved in rock. We use these parts to find out about organisms that lived on Earth long ago.

Why Scientists Study Fossils

Fossils (FAHS uhlz) can tell about what Earth was like many years ago. A **fossil** is part of an organism that lived long ago.

Bones, teeth, shells, and imprints can all be fossils. An imprint is the remains of a once-living thing that became pressed into mud or sand.

modern fern

fossil tree fern

VOCABULARY

era A major division of time. *(noun)*

fossil The preserved remains of an organism that lived long ago. *(noun)*

paleontologist A scientist who studies fossils and forms of life that no longer exist. *(noun)*

VOCABULARY SKILL: Word Origins

The word *fossil* comes from the Latin word *fodere*, which means "to dig." Read the definition of the word *fossil*. Then think about the meaning of its Latin origin. How do you think scientists find fossils?

_____

_____

 3.e. Students know that some kinds of organisms that once lived on Earth have completely disappeared; some of those organisms resembled organisms that are alive today.

1. A _____ is a scientist who studies fossils to learn about extinct plants and animals.

2. Fill in the ovals to tell what scientists can learn about living things from long ago by studying fossils.

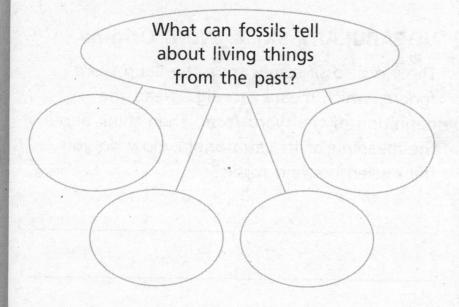

What can fossils tell about living things from the past?

People who learn about Earth and the things on it are scientists. A scientist who learns about fossils and living things that are extinct is called a **paleontologist** (pay lee ahn TAHL uh jihst). Paleontologists use fossils to learn about an organism and its environment.

A fossil of a fish can tell paleontologists about the fish. The fossil tells about the size and shape of the fish. The teeth show what it ate.

A fossil of a fish can tell paleontologists about the area where the fossil was found, too. They know that fish live in water. If the fossil is found on land, they guess that the area was once covered with water.

fish fossil

How a Fossil Forms

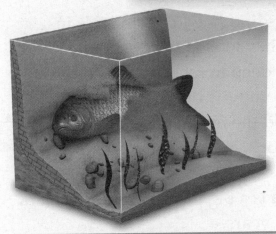

A living thing dies and is buried under sand and soil.

The sand and soil turn into rock over many years.

Over time, the rock wears away. The fossil can be seen.

3. Fill in the blanks to tell how a fossil forms.

> **1.** A _____ dies and is buried under _____ and _____.

> **2.** Over many years, the _____ and _____ turn into _____.

> **3.** Over time, the _____ wears away, and a _____ can be seen.

Summary Scientists can learn many things from fossils. How do scientists tell how old a fossil is?

_____

_____

_____

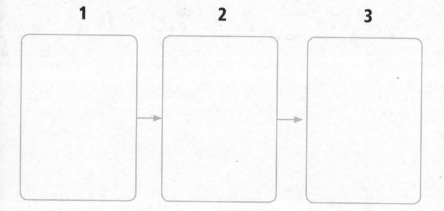

Sequence Describe how an organism becomes a fossil.

1	2	3

Dating Fossils

Paleontologists find how old a fossil is in different ways. They look at how deep the fossil is in rock. Fossils deep in rock are very old.

They can find out how old the rock is. That tells them how old the fossil is, too. If a fossil is found in an old rock, it is probably old, too.

Scientists break time into parts called eras (IHR uhz). An **era** is a big piece of time. Each era lasts many, many years.

This cat lived in our era about 16,000 years ago.

SEQUENCE

Describe how an organism becomes a fossil.

52

How Are Extinct and Living Things Alike?

3

Many extinct animals look like animals that live today. This helps scientists learn about the extinct animals.

Elephant Ancestors

There are only two species of elephants living today. And there are no other animals that look like elephants.

Both species have the same ancestors. An **ancestor** is a species that lived long ago that is like a species living today.

This animal is an ancestor to elephants.

VOCABULARY

ancestor A species or form of a species that lived long ago and to which modern species can be traced back. *(noun)*

relative A species that shares a common ancestor with another species. *(noun)*

trait A feature such as a body part or a behavior. *(noun)*

VOCABULARY SKILL: Picture Context

Look at the picture on page 53 and read the sentence that tells about it. Compare an elephant from today with the animal shown. Tell why you think the pictured animal is an *ancestor* of today's elephant.

_____

_____

_____

_____

 3.e. Students know that some kinds of organisms that once lived on Earth have completely disappeared; some of those organisms resembled organisms that are alive today.

1. Explain the difference between a relative and an ancestor.

_____

_____

_____

_____

2. List five traits that an elephant shares with its ancestors.

a. _____

b. _____

c. _____

d. _____

elephant ancestor

What traits do both of these species have?

elephant

Elephants do not have any close relatives that are living today. A **relative** is a species that has the same ancestor as another species. We say that relatives are related.

Relatives have many of the same traits. A **trait** is a body part or a way of acting. Big ears are a trait of elephants.

Animal Look-Alikes

The elephant is not the only species that looks like an extinct species. But not all species that look the same are related.

The emu is a large bird living today. It does not fly. It has a few of the same traits as an extinct bird. But fossils show that they are not related.

extinct bird

emu (living today)

3. An extinct animal looks like an animal that is alive today. Are they related? Why or why not?

_____

_____

_____

4. Look at the pictures of the birds on page 55. Circle the body parts that are the same. Then look at the shapes of the beaks. One beak is adapted to eating seeds. The other is adapted to eating meat. What do you think each bird ate?

_____

_____

_____

_____

_____

I Wonder . . . What animals alive today are related to dogs?

_____

_____

_____

5. Look at the picture of the rhinoceros and the extinct animal. What traits would make you think the animals are related?

_____

_____

_____

Some animals with the same traits are related. The rhinoceros is a big animal living today. It has a few of the same traits as an extinct species. Both eat leaves. Both have feet with three toes.

extinct animal

rhinoceros (living today)

Dinosaur-Bird Connections

Dinosaurs are extinct. There are no species living today that have all of the same traits as dinosaurs. But birds may have dinosaurs as ancestors.

Birds and dinosaurs have some of the same traits. Some dinosaurs had wings and feathers. Their hearts and lungs were like the ones in birds. Many scientists think these dinosaurs are the ancestors of birds living today.

extinct dinosaur

bird (living today)

COMPARE AND CONTRAST

In what ways are modern birds similar to their ancestors?

Summary Many extinct animals look like animals that live today. Choose an animal from the lesson. Compare it to its ancestor. Tell how the two animals are alike and different.

_____

_____

_____

_____

_____

Compare and Contrast In what ways are modern birds similar to their ancestors?

Modern Birds	Ancestors

Glossary

Write a short paragraph using the words on the page.

_____

_____

_____

_____

_____

_____

Glossary

ancestor (an SEHS tur) A species or form of a species that lived long ago and to which modern species can be traced back.

antepasado Especie o forma de especie que vivió hace mucho tiempo y con la cual se puede averiguar sobre los orígenes de una especie actual.

endangered species (ehn DAYN jurd SPEEsheez) A species that has so few members that the entire species is at risk of dying out.

especies en peligro Especie con tan pocos miembros que está en peligro de desaparición.

era (IHR uh) A major division of time.

era División grande del tiempo.

extinct species (ihk STIHNGKT SPEE sheez) A species that has died off.

especie extinta Especie que ha desaparecido.

Glossary

fossil (FAHS uhl) The preserved remains of an organism that lived long ago.

fósil Restos que se conservan de un organismo que vivió hace mucho tiempo.

paleontologist (pay lee ehn TAHL uh jihst) A scientist who studies fossils and forms of life that no longer exist.

paleontólogo Científico que estudia fósiles y formas de vida que ya no existen.

relative (reh LUH tihv) A species that shares a common ancestor with another species.

pariente Especie que comparte un antepasado común con otra especie.

species (SPEE sheez) A group of the same type of living thing that can mate and produce other living things of the same kind.

especie Grupo de seres vivos que pueden reproducirse y crear seres vivos del mismo tipo.

trait (trayt) A feature such as a body part or a behavior.

rasgo Característica propia de una parte del cuerpo o de un comportamiento.

 Visit www.eduplace.com to play puzzles and word games.

Find the English words that are like these Spanish words. List these words in the chart.

Spanish Word	English Word
era	
fósil	
palentólogo	

Chapter Review

WHAT DID YOU LEARN?

Vocabulary

❶ (Circle) the correct answer.

Comprehension

❷ _____ _____

❸ _____

❹ _____

Critical Thinking

❺ _____

_____

_____

_____

Think About What You Have Read

Vocabulary

❶ A species that is at risk of dying out is a/an _____.

   A) ancestor

   B) endangered species

   C) extinct species

   D) fossil

Comprehension

❷ A dodo is an example of a bird that is a/an _____.

❸ What can scientists learn from fossils?

❹ How do scientists learn about extinct species?

Critical Thinking

❺ How could you save a species that is endangered because of hunting?

WHAT DO YOU KNOW?

List one fact about each of these topics:

a. Telescopes _____

_____

b. The solar system _____

_____

c. Inner planets _____

_____

d. Outer planets _____

_____

Our Solar System

Contents

1 How Do Scientists Use Telescopes? 64

2 What Is the Solar System? 68

3 What Are the Inner Planets? 73

4 What Are the Outer Planets? 79

Glossary 84

WHAT DO YOU WANT TO KNOW?

Skim the pictures and headings in this chapter. List one thing you want to find out about each of these topics:

a. Telescopes _____

_____

b. The solar system _____

_____

c. Inner planets _____

_____

d. Outer planets _____

_____

Lesson Preview

VOCABULARY

magnify To make an object appear larger. *(verb)*

telescope A tool that makes distant objects appear larger, brighter, and sharper. *(noun)*

VOCABULARY SKILL: Word Origins

The word *telescope* comes from the Greek word *teleskopos*. *Tele* means "from a distance." *Skopos* means "seeing." Explain how these word parts relate to how a telescope works.

_____

_____

_____

_____

4.c. Students know telescopes make some distant objects in the sky, such as the Moon and planets, appear bigger. Many more stars can be seen using a telescope than can be seen without one.

1

How Do Scientists Use Telescopes?

Tools help scientists learn about Earth and the things around it.

Telescopes

Look up in the night sky. You can see the Moon. You can see small points of light called stars. You can even see planets. How can you see all of these things better?

A telescope can help you see them. A **telescope** is something that makes things far away look big and bright. When you make something look big, you **magnify** it.

telescope

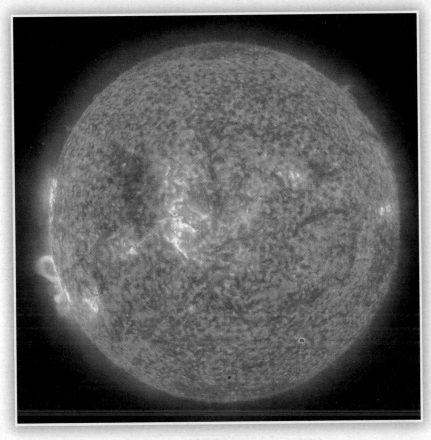

the Sun

It is not safe to look right at the Sun. It can hurt your eyes. You should never look straight at the Sun, even with a telescope. You can look at other stars, though. They are far away and will not hurt your eyes.

I Wonder . . . How is magnifying the image of an object like getting closer to it? What do you think?

_____

_____

_____

_____

_____

1. Why is it dangerous to look directly at the Sun?

_____

_____

2. Compare and contrast optical and radio telescopes.

Telescopes

Optical　　　　**Radio**

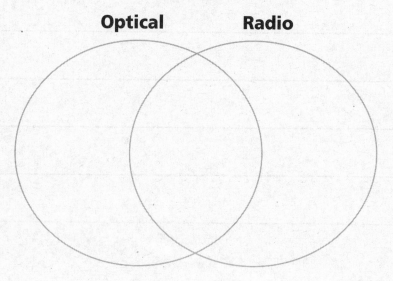

There are different kinds of telescopes. Some telescopes take in light. These are called optical (AHP tihk uhl) telescopes.

Other telescopes make pictures from radio waves. They are called radio telescopes.

All telescopes help scientists learn about things in space, or the area around Earth.

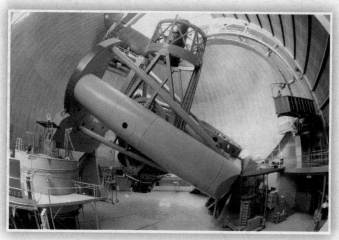

optical telescope

radio telescope

A Hubble Scrapbook

There is one telescope that is not on Earth. It is in space! It is called the Hubble Space Telescope. It moves around Earth.

The air around Earth changes how we see things in space. The Hubble takes pictures without Earth's air getting in the way. It helps scientists see things far off in space.

Hubble Space Telescope

picture from Hubble

PROBLEM AND SOLUTION

How is the Hubble able to help scientists see space more clearly?

Summary Telescopes are tools used by scientists.

Write a sentence telling how scientists use telescopes.

_____

_____

_____

Problem and Solution How is the Hubble able to help scientists see space more clearly than they could from Earth?

Problem	Solution

67

VOCABULARY

inner planets The four planets closest to the Sun—Mercury, Venus, Earth, and Mars. *(noun)*

moon A small, rounded body in orbit around a planet. *(noun)*

orbit To move in a path around an object. *(verb)*

outer planets The four planets farthest from the Sun—Jupiter, Saturn, Uranus, and Neptune. *(noun)*

planet A large body in space that moves around a star. *(noun)*

solar system The Sun, planets, moons, and other objects that orbit the Sun. *(noun)*

Sun The nearest star to Earth. *(noun)*

2 What Is the Solar System?

The solar system is made up of the Sun and the objects around it. Eight planets, their moons, and other things travel around the Sun.

The Sun and Planets

Stars are big balls of hot gas that give off heat and light. The **Sun** is a star. It is close to Earth. Other stars look small because they are so far away.

1.a. Students know energy comes from the Sun to Earth as light.
4.d. Students know that Earth is one of several planets that orbit the Sun and that the Moon orbits Earth.

A **planet** is a large body in space that moves around a star. A planet does not make light. We can see planets shine in the night sky because of light from the Sun. The planets reflect, or send back, the Sun's light.

Earth is one of eight planets that orbit the Sun. **Orbit** means to move in a path around something.

You can see Earth's moon at night, too. A **moon** is a small ball in orbit around a planet. Moons do not make light. Like planets, moons reflect light from the Sun. Most planets have one or more moons.

The Sun, planets, moons, and other things that orbit the Sun make up the **solar system** (SOH lur SIHS tuhm).

Eight planets orbit the Sun. Pluto is caller a dwarf planet.

1. Read the clues. Then identify the object or objects in space that are described.

Clue	Space Object
They do not make their own light.	
Earth is one of several that orbit the Sun.	
Some planets have none, some have one, and some have many.	
The star that is closest to Earth.	
The Sun, planets, moons and all other things that orbit the Sun.	

2. List the inner planets in order from the Sun.

a. _____

b. _____

c. _____

d. _____

3. What two things do the inner planets get from the Sun?

a. _____

b. _____

The Inner Planets

Mercury (MUR kyuh ree), Venus (VEE nuhs), Earth, and Mars (mahrz) are the **inner planets**. They are the planets closest to the Sun. They get a lot of heat and light from the Sun.

1 Mercury is the first planet from the Sun. It is hot in the day and very cold at night.

2 Venus is the second planet from the Sun. It is covered by gas and is very hot.

3 Earth is the third planet from the Sun. As far as we know, it is the only planet that has living things.

4 Mars is the fourth planet from the Sun. It has many craters and mountains.

The Outer Planets

Jupiter (JOO pih tur), Saturn (SAT urn), Uranus (YUR uh nuhs), and Neptune (NEHP toon) are the **outer planets**. They are cold and dark because they are far from the Sun. These planets are made of gas and have many moons. Pluto (PLOO toh) is called a dwarf planet. It is small and made of rocks.

6 Saturn is the sixth planet from the Sun. It has rings made of dust, ice, and rocks.

5 Jupiter is the fifth planet from the Sun. It is the largest planet.

8 Neptune is the eighth planet from the Sun. It is blue.

7 Uranus is the seventh planet from the Sun. It is the only planet that spins, or turns, on its side.

Pluto is a dwarf planet. It is smaller than the planets and very far from the Sun.

4. List the outer planets in order from the Sun. Include one dwarf planet.

a. _____

b. _____

c. _____

d. _____

e. _____

5. Look at the list you just made.

a. Put a ✔ next to the largest planet.

b. Circle the planet that spins on its side.

c. Identify the object that is farthest from the Sun. Write "dwarf planet" next to this object's name.

71

Summary The solar system is made up of the Sun, the planets, their moons, and other objects traveling around the Sun.

What do we call the amount of time it takes for a planet to orbit the Sun? How long is one full spin?

_____

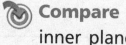 **Compare and Contrast** How are the inner planets and outer planets alike? How are they different?

Inner Planets   **Outer Planets**

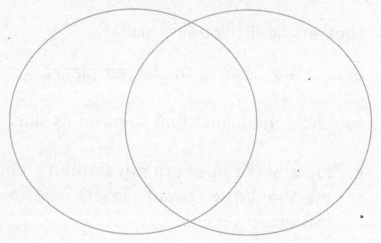

Planets in Motion

Planets spin like tops as they orbit the Sun. Earth's day is one full spin. It is 24 hours long. Some planets spin faster than Earth. Some planets do not spin as fast as Earth.

Planets also take different times to orbit the Sun. Planets that are far from the Sun have a long way to go. They take a long time to orbit. Planets that are close to the Sun do not have as far to go. They take less time to obit.

The time it takes Earth to orbit the Sun is called a year. Earth's year is about 365 days long. Mercury is close to the Sun so it orbits in less time than Earth. It takes only 88 Earth days to orbit the Sun.

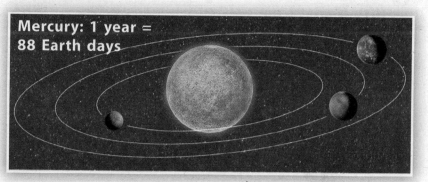

Mercury: 1 year = 88 Earth days

COMPARE AND CONTRAST

How are the inner planets and outer planets alike? How are they different?

What Are the Inner Planets?

3

Mercury, Venus, Earth, and Mars are the inner planets. They are small, ball-shaped, and made of rock.

Mercury

Mercury is the first planet from the Sun. It is only about the size of Earth's moon. Mercury is so close to the Sun that it is very, very hot during the day. At night it is very cold.

Mercury moves through space very quickly, but it spins slowly. It does not have any moons.

Mercury orbits quickly, but spins slowly.

VOCABULARY

space probe A craft that helps scientists explore outer space. *(noun)*

VOCABULARY SKILL: Word Origins

Mercury is one of the inner planets that you will learn more about in this lesson. The Romans named this planet after their messenger god. Mercury, the messenger, had to run very fast from place to place. What can you infer from this information about the speed of Mercury's orbit around the Sun?

_____

_____

 4.d. Students know that Earth is one of several planets that orbit the Sun and that the Moon orbits Earth.

73

1. Read each clue. Tell whether it describes Mercury, Venus, or Earth. Some clues apply to more than one planet.

Clue	Planet
Planet closest to the Sun	
Has a day that is longer than its year	
Has no moons	
Has one moon	
Only planet in the solar system that has living things	
Is very hot	
Has water	

Venus

Venus is the second planet from the Sun. It is about the same size as Earth.

Venus spins so slowly that its "day" is longer than its year! That means that Venus orbits all the way around the Sun in less time than it takes to make one full spin. It does not have any moons.

Venus is covered by thick clouds.

Earth's distance from the Sun and the air around Earth help keep the planet warm.

Earth

Earth is the third planet from the Sun. It is where we live. It is the only planet in the solar system that we know can have living things. Living things need air and water. Earth has both of these things. The air around Earth keeps it from getting too hot or too cold.

Planets move in two ways. Earth spins every 24 hours. This makes day and night. Earth also orbits the Sun about every 365 days. This makes one year. Earth has one moon.

2. List the two ways that Earth moves. Tell how long each movement takes.

a. _____

b. _____

I Wonder . . . What factors would cause Earth to be the only planet we know of that has living things? What do you think?

_____

_____

_____

3. If you were to draw a picture of Mars, what color crayon would you use?

_____

4. List three facts about Mars.

   a. _____

   b. _____

   c. _____

5. How does the length of a day on Mars compare with the length of a day on Earth?

_____

_____

6. How does the length of a year on Mars compare with the length of a year on Earth?

_____

_____

Mars

Mars is the fourth planet from the Sun. It is called the Red Planet. It is covered with red rocks. Scientists think living things may once have lived on Mars. But no signs of life have been found yet.

Mars and Earth spin at about the same speed. That means that one day is about the same on the two planets. But a year on Mars is almost twice as long as a year on Earth. Mars has two moons.

Mars is farther from the Sun so it is colder than Earth.

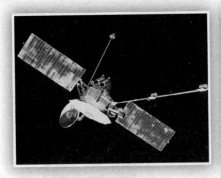

space probes

Exploring the Inner Planets

It is hard for scientists to study the planets because they are so far away from Earth. For years, scientists have used telescopes to study the other planets.

Now they use space probes, too. A **space probe** is a craft that helps scientists learn about space. Space probes carry tools, but not people. The probes have cameras and other tools for taking pictures. They send the information back to Earth. Then scientists can learn from it.

7. What is a space probe?

_____

_____

8. What happens to the information space probes gather?

_____

_____

_____

I Wonder . . . Why would scientists build space probes that do not carry people into space?

_____

_____

_____

_____

Summary The inner planets are Mercury, Venus, Earth, and Mars. Earth is the only planet that has life.

List three traits that the inner planets share.

a. _____

b. _____

c. _____

🎯 **Main Idea** How do space probes help scientists to study other planets?

_____

_____

_____

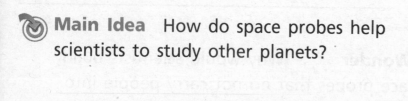

This is a rover. It is one of two rovers that landed on Mars in 2004. The rovers studied rocks and soil. They looked for signs that water was once on Mars.

MAIN IDEA

How do space probes help scientists to study other planets?

What Are the Outer Planets?

4

The planets farthest from the Sun are called the outer planets. They are Jupiter, Saturn, Uranus, and Neptune.

Jupiter

Jupiter is the fifth planet from the Sun. It is bigger than all of the other planets put together! Jupiter has a big storm called the Great Red Spot. It is the size of two Earths!

A **gas giant** is a very large planet made up of gases. Jupiter, Saturn, Uranus, and Neptune are the four gas giants. They are covered with clouds.

Jupiter spins very fast. Its day is only about 10 hours long. Jupiter has at least 63 moons, but scientists are looking for even more.

This is the Great Red Spot on Jupiter. It is a big storm.

VOCABULARY

gas giant A very large planet made up mostly of gases. *(noun)*

VOCABULARY SKILL: Word Phrases

Pluto was once classified as a planet. But in 2006, astronomers changed its classification to *dwarf planet*. A *dwarf* is a plant, animal, or object that is much smaller in size than most others of its kind. Use this information to write your own definition of a dwarf planet.

_____

_____

 4.d. Students know that Earth is one of several planets that orbit the Sun and that the Moon orbits Earth.

1. What is a gas giant?

   _____

2. Compare Jupiter and Saturn.

   a. Which planet is bigger? _____

   b. Which planet has rings? _____

   c. Which planet has a giant storm called

      the Great Red Spot? _____

3. Find the photo that shows Saturn with its rings. Now look at the larger photo that is a close up of the rings. What are these rings made of?

   _____

Saturn has rings around it.

Saturn

Saturn is the sixth planet from the Sun. It is the second largest. Saturn has rings around it. The rings are made of pieces of ice, dust, and rocks. Most of the pieces are very small. Some are as big as houses!

Saturn spins fast, like Jupiter. Its day is only about 11 hours long. Saturn has at least 47 moons.

Uranus

Uranus is the seventh planet from the Sun. It is the third largest. About 64 Earths could fit into Uranus!

Uranus is the only planet that spins on its side. This makes each side of the planet have "day" for half the year and "night" for the other half.

Uranus is one of the gas giants. A gas makes it a beautiful blue-green color. It has at least 27 moons.

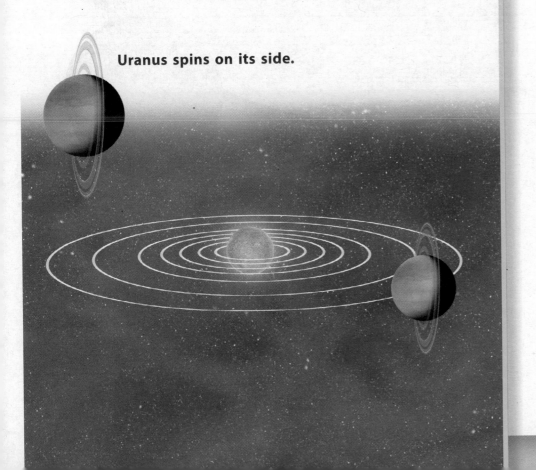

Uranus spins on its side.

4. List four facts about Uranus.

a. _____

b. _____

c. _____

d. _____

I Wonder . . . It takes Uranus 84 Earth years to orbit the Sun. A point on the surface of Uranus spends half of that time in darkness. How long would a day be on Uranus?

_____

_____

_____

_____

_____

5. How does Neptune compare in size with the other gas giants?

_____

6. How long does it take Neptune, in Earth years, to orbit the Sun? Tell why it takes Neptune so long.

_____

_____

_____

Triton

Neptune has at least 13 moons. Triton is the name of its largest moon.

Neptune

Neptune is the eighth planet from the Sun. It is the fourth-largest planet, but it is the smallest of the gas giants. Neptune is so far from the Sun that it takes 165 Earth years to orbit once!

Neptune is very cold and has very strong winds. It has at least 13 moons.

Pluto

Pluto was once known as the ninth planet. Today it is known as a dwarf planet. The dwarf planets are small, round objects that orbit in the same way as planets. Pluto is made of rock and ice. It has three moons.

Pluto's orbit is different from the orbits of the other planets. The shape of its orbit is a very long oval. Pluto's orbit is so stretched out that it crosses Neptune's orbit every 248 years.

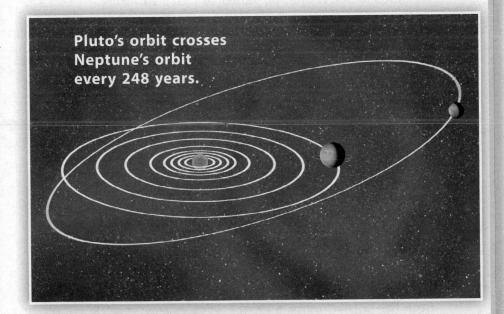

Pluto's orbit crosses Neptune's orbit every 248 years.

SEQUENCE

Which two planets are next to Jupiter?

Summary The planets farthest from the Sun are called the outer planets. They are all gas giants, except for Pluto.

How is Pluto different from the outer planets?

_____

_____

 Sequence Which two planets are next to Jupiter?

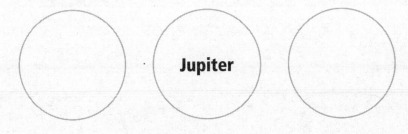

Jupiter

_____   _____

Draw a picture illustrating the words *orbit* and *moon*. Add arrows to show the motion of the moon.

gas giant (gas JY ent) A very large planet made up mostly of gases.

gigante gaseoso Planeta muy grande compuesto en su mayor parte por gases.

inner planets (IHN ur PLAN ihts) The four planets closest to the Sun—Mercury, Venus, Earth, and Mars.

planetas interiores Son los cuatro planetas más cercanos al Sol: Mercurio, Venus, la Tierra y Marte.

magnify (MAG nuh fy) To make an object appear larger.

aumentar Hacer que un objeto parezca más grande.

moon (moon) A small, rounded body in orbit around a planet.

luna Cuerpo pequeño y redondo que orbita alrededor de un planeta.

orbit (OHR biht) To move in a path around an object.

orbitar Hacer un recorrido alrededor de un objeto.

outer planets (OW tur PLAN ihts) The four planets farthest from the Sun—Jupiter, Saturn, Uranus, and Neptune.

planetas exteriores Son los cuatro planetas más alejados del Sol: Júpiter, Saturno, Urano y Neptuno.

Glossary

planet (PLAN iht) A large body in space that moves around a star.

planeta Cuerpo sideral de gran tamaño que se mueve alrededor de una estrella.

solar system (SOH lur SIHS tuhm) The Sun, planets, moons, and other objects that orbit the Sun.

sistema solar Está formado por el Sol, los planetas, las lunas y otros objetos que orbitan alrededor del Sol.

space probe (spays prohb) A craft that helps scientists explore outer space.

sonda espacial Máquina que ayuda a los científicos a explorar el espacio exterior.

Sun (suhn) The nearest star to Earth.

Sol La estrella más cercana a la Tierra.

telescope (TEHL ih skohp) A tool that makes distant objects appear larger, brighter, and sharper.

telescopio Instrumento que hace parecer más grandes, brillantes y claros los objetos distantes.

Visit www.eduplace.com to play puzzles and word games.

Circle the English words and their meanings for all the glossary words.

Chapter Review

WHAT DID YOU LEARN?

Vocabulary

❶ (Circle) the correct answer.

Comprehension

❷ _____

❸ _____

_____

❹ _____

_____

Critical Thinking

❺ _____

_____

_____

_____

Responding

Think About What You Have Read

Vocabulary

❶ A body that orbits the Sun and does not make light is a/an _____.

  A) moon

  B) star

  C) planet

  D) space probe

Comprehension

❷ What tool can you use to see objects in space more clearly?

❸ What do the inner planets have in common?

❹ What is a gas giant?

Critical Thinking

❺ If Pluto were still classified as a planet, would you say it has more in common with the outer planets or the inner planets? Why?

WHAT DO YOU KNOW?

List one fact about each of these topics:

a. What causes day and night _____

_____

_____

b. What causes the seasons _____

_____

_____

c. The phases of the moon _____

_____

_____

d. Stars _____

_____

Cycles and Patterns in Space

Contents

1 What Causes Day and Night? 90

2 What Causes the Seasons? 94

3 What Are the Phases of the Moon? . . 99

4 What Is a Star? 106

Glossary 111

WHAT DO YOU WANT TO KNOW?

Skim the pictures and headings in this chapter. List one thing you want to find out about each of these topics:

a. Day and night _____

_____

_____

b. The seasons _____

_____

_____

c. Phases of the Moon _____

_____

_____

d. Stars _____

_____

Lesson Preview

VOCABULARY

axis An imaginary line through the center of an object. *(noun)*

rotate To turn on an axis. *(verb)*

VOCABULARY SKILL: Synonyms

Synonyms are words that mean almost the same thing. A synonym for *rotate* is *spin*. Earth rotates much like a top. Draw a picture of a top. Use an arrow to show how the top *rotates* or *spins*.

4.e. Students know the position of the Sun in the sky changes during the course of the day and from season to season.
1.a. Students know energy comes from the Sun to Earth as light.
2.a. Students know sunlight can be blocked to make shadows.

1 What Causes Day and Night?

Earth turns. This makes the Sun's place in the sky change during the day. As Earth turns, the Sun appears to go up, move across the sky, and then go back down.

Rotating Earth

While you eat breakfast, it is the middle of the night in Greece. How can this be?

You know about one way the planets move. They orbit, or move in a path, around the Sun.

California

Greece

When it is morning in California, it is night in Greece.

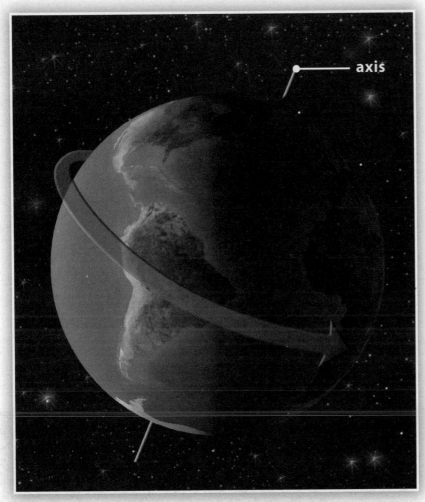

axis

Earth rotates on its axis.

As the planets orbit, they also rotate (ROH tayt). To **rotate** is to turn on an axis (AK sihs). An **axis** is an imaginary line through the middle of an object. It is not a real line that you can see or touch. Earth's axis goes through the North and South Poles.

1. When it is morning in California, what time of day is it on the other side of the Earth in Greece?

_____

_____

2. What is an axis?

_____

_____

3. (Circle) the object that rotates, causing day and night.

Sun   Earth

4. Look at the picture. On the side of Earth that is lit by the Sun, write the letter *D* for daytime. On the side of Earth that is dark, write the letter *N* for nighttime

5. Complete the table to tell how the Sun and shadows change during the day.

Time of Day	Sun's Place in Sky	Shadows
Early morning		long shadows point away from the Sun
Noon		
Late afternoon		

Watch the Sun from morning to night. It looks as if the Sun moves across the sky. But it is Earth that moves. The Sun stays in the same place.

Early in the morning, the Sun seems to rise, or come up. This is when the part of Earth where you live faces the Sun.

As the day goes on, Earth is still rotating. The Sun seems to move across the sky, but it is Earth that is turning.

As Earth keeps rotating, your side of Earth turns away from the Sun. The Sun looks as if it sets, or goes down. It gets dark without the Sun's light. Night begins on your side of Earth. Now it is day on the other side of Earth.

The side of Earth with the flag faces the Sun. It is daytime there.

Sunrise and Sunset

In the morning, the Sun rises in the east. As Earth turns, the Sun seems to move higher in the sky. The Sun seems to be the highest at noon. Earth continues to turn, and the Sun seems to move until it sets in the west.

As Earth turns, the Sun's place in the sky changes. The Sun's light hits Earth in different ways at different times of the day. This makes shadows change through the day, too.

The Sun is low in the sky in the morning and evening. Then shadows are long. The Sun is high in the sky at noon. Then shadows are short.

Changing Shadow Length

sunlight · sunlight · sunlight

early morning · noon · late afternoon

CAUSE AND EFFECT

What causes the Sun to seem to move across the sky?

Summary The Sun's place in the sky changes during the day because Earth rotates, or turns, on its axis. As Earth rotates, the Sun seems to rise in the east, move across the sky, and then set in the west.

When does the Sun seem to be highest in the sky?

_____

_____

Cause and Effect What causes the Sun to seem to move across the sky?

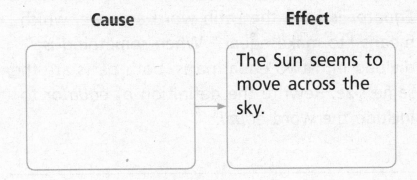

Cause	Effect
	The Sun seems to move across the sky.

VOCABULARY

equator An imaginary line that circles Earth halfway between the North and South Poles. *(noun)*

revolve To move in a path around another object. *(verb)*

season One of the four parts of the year—spring, summer, fall, and winter. *(noun)*

VOCABULARY SKILL: Word Origins

Read the definition of the word *equator*. *Equator* is from the Latin word *aequare*, which means "to make equal." When something is divided into two equal parts, both parts are the same size. Rewrite the definition of *equator* to include the word *equal*.

_____

_____

4.e. Students know the position of the Sun in the sky changes during the course of the day and from season to season.
4.d. Students know that Earth is one of several planets that orbit the Sun and that the Moon orbits Earth.

2 What Causes the Seasons?

The tilt of Earth's axis causes changes in the seasons and in the Sun's place in the sky.

Revolving Earth

You learned that Earth orbits, or moves in a path, around the Sun. To move in a path around another object is to **revolve** (rih VAHLV). It takes one year for Earth to revolve around the Sun one time. The path it takes is in the shape of a flat, stretched circle.

The Seasons

Spring

Winter

Fall

As Earth revolves, its axis is tilted. The Sun's light strikes Earth in different ways at different times of the year. The tilt makes Earth's seasons (SEE zuhns) change. A **season** is one of the four parts of the year. The seasons are spring, summer, fall, and winter.

The **equator** (ee KWAY tur) is an imaginary line that circles Earth. It divides Earth into two halves called hemispheres. You live in the Northern Hemisphere, or the half of Earth that is close to the North Pole.

In June, the Northern Hemisphere tilts toward the Sun. It gets a lot of light, so it is summer here. In December, the Northern Hemisphere tilts away from the Sun. It does not get a lot of light, so it is winter here.

When you are in summer, people in the southern half of Earth are in winter. When you are in winter, people there are in summer.

Summer

1. How long does it takes Earth to revolve around the Sun once?

_____

2. List the four seasons.

   a. _____

   b. _____

   c. _____

   d. _____

3. Look back at your list.
   a. What season is it where you live when the Northern Hemisphere is tilted toward the Sun? Circle that season.

   b. What season is it where you live when the Northern Hemisphere is tilted away from the Sun? Draw a box around that season.

4. Draw an arrow to show the direction in which the Sun appears to move across the sky during the day.

east   west

5. Draw a picture to show where in the sky the Sun would be at noon on a day in June. Your drawing should show the ground with trees or a building, as well as the sky.

Changing Position of the Sun

The Sun seems to move from east to west across the sky. The Sun is in a different place in different seasons, too.

When you are outside at noon on a June day, the Sun seems to be very high in the sky. It is very hot. When you are outside at noon on a December day, the Sun seems to be much lower in the sky. It is not as warm. Why?

summer in the Northern Hemisphere

winter in the Northern Hemisphere

In June, the Northern Hemisphere tilts toward the Sun. The Sun seems to be high in the sky. Because this part of Earth faces the Sun, it gets a lot of light. It is warm.

In December, the Northern Hemisphere tilts away from the Sun. The Sun seems to be low in the sky. Because this part of Earth is tilted away from the Sun, it does not get as much light. It is not as warm.

6. Complete the chart to compare summer and winter in the Northern Hemisphere.

Condition	In Summer (June)	In Winter (December)
Tilt of Northern Hemisphere		
Sun's height in sky		
Weather		
Amount of light		

Summary As Earth revolves around the Sun, the tilt of Earth's axis causes changes in the seasons and in the Sun's place in the sky.

Tell how Earth's tilt changes the number of daylight hours in summer. Use the Northern Hemisphere as your example.

_____

_____

_____

_____

_____

Sequence In what season do the days have the fewest hours of daylight?

_____

Length of Day and Night Changes

You may have noticed that it is dark when you eat dinner in the winter. Even if you eat at the same time every day, it is light out when you eat dinner in the summer. This change is caused by the tilt of Earth's axis.

7:00 P.M. in June in California

You have summer when your part of Earth tilts toward the Sun. In summer, you face the Sun for more hours than you face away from it. That means you have more hours of daylight and fewer hours of darkness. Your days are long. It stays light into the evening.

7:00 P.M. in December in California

You have winter when your part of Earth tilts away from the Sun. Then you are turned away from the Sun for more hours than you face it. That means you have fewer hours of daylight and more hours of darkness. Your days are shorter. It gets dark early.

SEQUENCE

In what season do the days have the fewest hours of daylight?

What Are the Phases of the Moon?

The Moon seems to change shape. These changes are caused by the way sunlight hits the Moon as it revolves around Earth.

Earth's Moon

The Moon is a ball-shaped object made of rock. It revolves around Earth once every $27\frac{1}{3}$ days. The Moon also rotates on its axis once in the same amount of time. So the same side of the Moon always faces Earth. This is called the near side.

The Moon does not make its own light. It reflects, or bounces back, the Sun's light. The reflected sunlight makes the near side of the Moon look bright. The other side is dark, so you cannot see it.

— the Moon

VOCABULARY

crescent moon The phase of the Moon when a thin part of the Moon's near side is sunlit. *(noun)*

full moon The phase of the Moon when all of the Moon's near side is sunlit. *(noun)*

new moon The phase of the Moon when the Moon's near side receives no sunlight. *(noun)*

phases of the Moon The different ways the Moon looks throughout the month. *(noun)*

quarter moon The phase of the Moon when half of the Moon's near side is sunlit. *(noun)*

waning moon The phases of the Moon when a decreasing amount of the Moon's near side is sunlit. *(noun)*

waxing moon The phases of the Moon when an increasing amount of the Moon's near side is sunlit. *(noun)*

 4.b. Students know how the Moon's appearance changes during its four-week cycle.
2.b. Students know mirrors and other surfaces reflect light.

99

1. Tell why the same side of the Moon always faces Earth.

_____

_____

2. Circle the sentence that tells what makes the near side of the Moon look bright.

   a. The Moon makes its own light.

   b. The Moon reflects light from the Sun.

Sun

Earth

Moon

The Moon does not make light. It reflects light from the Sun.

Even though the same side of the Moon always faces Earth, it seems to change shape. This is because the near side of the Moon gets different amounts of sunlight at different times.

The Moon revolves and rotates the same way every $27\frac{1}{3}$ days. That means that the Moon will look the same tonight as it will in about one month. In that time, the Moon takes on eight different forms. The different ways the Moon looks throughout the month are called the **phases of the Moon**.

These pictures show how the phases of the Moon look from Earth.

7. Quarter Moon

8. Waning Moon

6. Waning Moon

1. New Moon

5. Full Moon

2. Waxing Moon

4. Waxing Moon

3. Quarter Moon

3. Complete the diagram to tell what causes the Moon to seem to change shape.

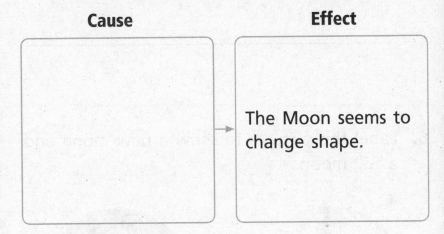

Cause

Effect

The Moon seems to change shape.

4. What is the changing shape of the Moon called?

_____

5. What phase of the Moon occurs when all of the Moon's near side is sunlit?

_____

6. Label the pictures to show a new moon and a full moon.

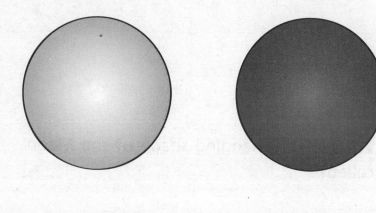

_____   _____

The first phase is called a **new moon**. The Moon's near side does not get any sunlight. The near side of the Moon is dark, and you cannot see it.

The second phase is called a **waxing moon**. A little bit of the Moon's near side gets sunlight. This waxing moon is in a thin shape called a **crescent** (KREHS uhnt) **moon**.

The third phase is called a **quarter moon**. Half the Moon's near side, or one quarter of the whole Moon, faces the Sun. From Earth, the quarter moon looks like half of a ball.

The fourth phase is another waxing moon. But this time three-quarters of the near side gets sunlight. This waxing moon looks like a circle with a small bite taken out of it.

The fifth phase is a **full moon**. The Moon has revolved halfway around Earth. The whole near side gets sunlight. From Earth, the full moon looks like a whole ball.

The sixth phase is a **waning moon**. A little bit less of the Moon's near side gets sunlight. This waxing moon looks like another circle with a small bite taken out of it.

The seventh phase is another quarter moon. Like the third phase, it looks like half of a ball to people on Earth.

The eighth phase is the last one. It is another waning moon. This moon looks like the second phase. They are both thin crescents. After this phase, a new moon happens again and the phases start all over again.

7. Number the drawings of the phases of the Moon in order. Start with new moon as 1.

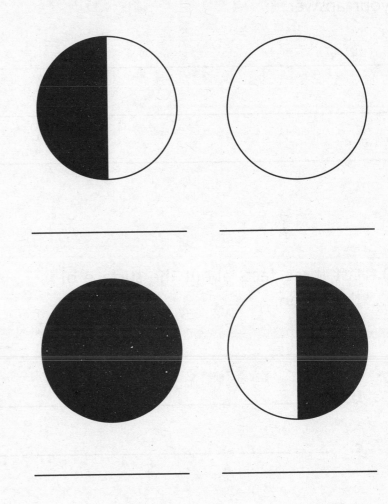

103

I Wonder . . . If the Moon and Earth never moved, would the Moon have phases? Explain your answer.

_____

_____

_____

9. List three facts about the surface of the Moon.

   a. _____

   b. _____

   c. _____

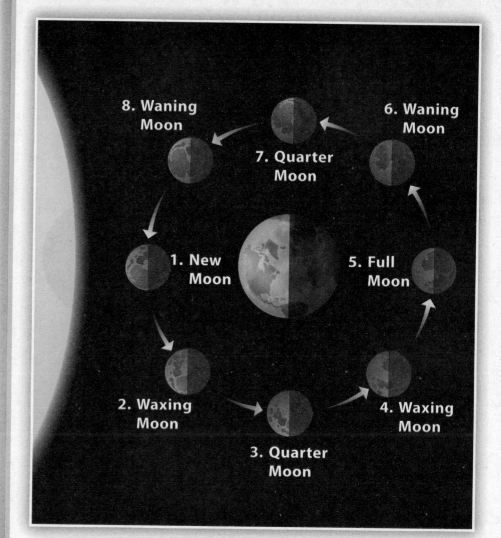

The Moon in Motion

The Moon's phases are based on where the Moon is as it revolves around Earth. These pictures show where the Moon is in each phase.

A Closer Look at the Moon

The Moon is made of dark rock and dust. It is covered with mountains, flat areas, and craters. A crater is a dent that is shaped like a bowl. It is made when an object from space hits the Moon or a planet.

There is no air or water on the Moon. Living things need air and water, so there are no living things on the Moon. The Moon gets very hot in the day and very cold at night.

the Moon

Summary The Moon's shape seems to change from a crescent to a half circle, to a whole circle, and then back again. These changes are caused by the way sunlight strikes the Moon as the Moon revolves around Earth.

Tell why there are no living things on the Moon.

_____

_____

Compare and Contrast What are two different ways that the Moon moves?

_____

_____

COMPARE AND CONTRAST

What are two different ways that the Moon moves?

VOCABULARY

constellation A group of stars that forms a pattern shaped like an animal, person, or object. *(noun)*

star A ball of hot gases that gives off light and other forms of energy. *(noun)*

VOCABULARY SKILL: Word Origins

Read the definition of the word *constellation*. *Stella* is a Latin word, which means "star." *Con* is a prefix meaning "with". Together, *con* and *stella* mean "with stars." Write your own definition of *constellation* to include the words *with stars*.

_____

_____

 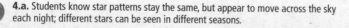 **4.a.** Students know star patterns stay the same, but appear to move across the sky each night; different stars can be seen in different seasons.

4 What Is a Star?

Stars are big balls of hot gas. From Earth, stars appear to be small points of light because they are very far away. Stars stay in the same place but seem to change because Earth is always moving.

The Night Sky

A **star** is a ball of hot gas that gives off light. Stars look like tiny dots of light. But they are not tiny at all. They only look small because they are very, very far away.

Stars come in different sizes. Some stars are only about 20 km across. But some stars are bigger than 1,000 times the distance from Earth to the Moon!

> **Stars look small in the night sky because they are very far from Earth.**

The Sun is the closest star to Earth.

The Sun

The Sun is a star. It is the largest thing in the solar system. More than 1 million Earths would fit inside the Sun! But, compared to other stars, the Sun is not very big. The Sun looks much larger than other stars because it is so much closer to Earth than any other star.

The Sun gives us light and heat. Living things could not live on Earth without the Sun.

1. A star is a ball of hot gas that gives off light. Compare the size of the Sun to the size of other stars

   _____

2. Tell why the Sun looks larger than the other stars.

   _____

3. List two things that the Sun gives Earth.

   a. _____

   b. _____

4. Star patterns are called _____.

5. How many constellations are there?

_____

6. Look at the two pictures that show the Big Dipper. Circle the picture that shows the Big Dipper low in the sky.

7. What caused the change in where the Big Dipper appears?

_____

_____

Constellations

Look up at the sky. The stars make patterns that look like things you know. Some patterns look like animals. Some look like people or things we see every day.

These patterns in the sky are called constellations (kahn stuh LAY shuhns). A **constellation** is a group of stars that makes a pattern shaped like an animal, person, or object. There are 88 constellations.

The Big Dipper is a pattern of seven stars that look like a big pot.

You know that the Sun appears to move across the sky each day. At night, the stars appear to move across the sky. These are both caused by the rotation of Earth.

As Earth rotates, the part of the sky that you see changes. That makes the constellations seem to move. But it is really Earth that is moving. The shape of the constellations does not change, but their place in the sky does.

The Big Dipper looks like it has moved, but it is Earth that moves.

8. Draw and label the Big Dipper.

Summary A star is a huge ball of hot gases. When seen from Earth, most stars look like small points of light because they are very far away. They form patterns that change position in the sky as Earth rotates and revolves.

Tell why you can see different stars at different times of the year.

_____

_____

 Draw Conclusions Why do the stars appear to move during the night?

_____

Seasonal Constellations

Earth revolves around the Sun. As it does, the part of the sky that you see changes. You can see different constellations at different times of the year. That means that you may not be able to see the same stars in the summer that you see in the winter.

In the summer, you can see Scorpius (SKAWR pee uhs). It is a group of stars that look like a scorpion. In the winter, you can see the Big Dog. One of the stars in the Big Dog is called Sirius (SIHR ee uhs). It is the brightest star in the night sky.

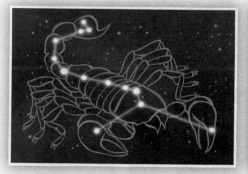
The Scorpius Constellation

The Big Dog Constellation

DRAW CONCLUSIONS

Why do the stars appear to move during the night?

axis (AK sihs) An imaginary line through the center of an object.

eje Línea imaginaria que pasa por el centro de un objeto.

constellation (kahn stuh LAY shuhn) A group of stars that forms a pattern shaped like an animal, person, or object.

constelación Grupo de estrellas que forman una figura parecida a un animal, persona u objeto.

crescent moon (KREHS uhnt moon) The phase of the Moon when a thin part of the Moon's near side is sunlit.

luna creciente o menguante La fase de la Luna en la cual una parte delgada de la luna recibe luz del Sol.

equator (ee KWAY tur) An imaginary line that circles Earth halfway between the North and South Poles.

ecuador Línea imaginaria que rodea a la Tierra y está a la misma distancia del Polo Norte que del Polo Sur.

equator

Draw a picture that shows the meaning of one of the glossary terms.

Circle the words on this page that tell about phases of the Moon.

full moon (ful moon) The phase of the Moon when all of the Moon's near side is sunlit.

luna llena Fase de la Luna en la cual todo su lado más cercano recibe luz del Sol.

new moon (noo moon) The phase of the Moon when the Moon's near side receives no sunlight.

luna nueva Fase de la Luna durante la cual su lado más cercano no recibe luz del Sol.

phases of the Moon (FAYZ ihz uhf thuh moon) The different ways the Moon looks throughout the month.

fases de la luna Distintos aspectos que toma la Luna durante el mes.

quarter moon (KWAHR tur moon) The phase of the Moon when half of the Moon's near side is sunlit.

media luna Fase de la Luna en la que la mitad más cercana recibe luz del Sol.

revolve (rih VAHLV) To move in a path around another object.

girar Moverse siguiendo un recorrido alrededor de otro objeto.

Glossary

rotate (ROH tayt) To turn on an axis.

  rotar Girar alrededor de un eje.

season (SEE zuhn) One of the four parts of the year— spring, summer, fall, and winter.

  estación Cada una de las cuatro partes del año: primavera, verano, otoño e invierno.

star (stahr) A ball of hot gases that gives off light and other forms of energy.

  estrella Bola de gases calientes que produce luz y otras formas de energía.

waning moon (WAY nihng moon) The phases of the Moon when a decreasing amount of the Moon's near side is sunlit.

  luna menguante Fase de la Luna en la cual disminuye la cantidad de luz del Sol que recibe su lado más cercano.

waxing moon (WAHK zihng moon) The phases of the Moon when an increasing amount of the Moon's near side is sunlit.

  luna creciente Fase de la Luna en la cual aumenta la cantidad de luz del Sol que recibe su lado más cercano.

 Visit www.eduplace.com to play puzzles and word games.

Find the English words that are like these Spanish words. List the English words in the chart.

Spanish Word	English Word
constelación	
ecuador	
rotar	

WHAT DID YOU LEARN?

Vocabulary

❶ (Circle) the correct answer.

Comprehension

❷ _____

_____

❸ _____

_____

_____

❹ _____

_____

Critical Thinking

❺ _____

_____

Think About What You Have Read

Vocabulary

❶ The ways the Moon looks when seen from Earth are the _____.

   A) constellations

   B) phases of the Moon

   C) new moons

   D) seasons

Comprehension

❷ What causes day and night?

❸ Why does the Moon's shape look different on different nights?

❹ Why does the Sun look larger than the other stars you can see?

Critical Thinking

❺ How is the movement of the Moon similar to that of Earth?

WHAT DO YOU KNOW?
Write one fact to show what you know about each of these topics.

a. What matter is _____

_____

_____

b. What the forms of matter are _____

_____

_____

c. How heat can change matter _____

_____

_____

Properties of Matter

Contents

1 What Is Matter?.................. 118

2 What Are the Forms of Matter? 124

3 How Does Heat Change Matter? ... 132

Glossary 139

WHAT DO YOU WANT TO KNOW?
Skim the pictures and headings in this chapter. Write a question you have about the properties of matter.

_____

_____

_____

Write a question you have about how heat can change matter.

_____

_____

_____

VOCABULARY

atom The smallest particle of some kinds of matter that has the properties of that kind of matter. *(noun)*

matter Anything that has mass and takes up space. *(noun)*

physical change A change in size, shape, or form of matter. *(noun)*

physical property A trait of matter that can be measured or observed with the senses. *(noun)*

VOCABULARY SKILL: Word Context

Which sentence below gives you a definition of matter? How do you know?

Everything around you is made up of matter.

Matter is anything that has mass and takes up space.

_____

_____

1.e. Students know solid, liquid, and gas are three forms of matter.
1.h. Students know all matter is made of particles called atoms that are too small to see.

118

1 What Is Matter?

Everything around you is made up of matter. Matter is made up of small parts called atoms. Atoms are too small to see.

Properties of Matter

Look around the room. Everything around you is made up of matter. **Matter** is anything that has mass and takes up space. Mass is the amount of matter in an object.

Even the air around you is matter. You cannot see air, but it takes up space. Try blowing up a balloon. The balloon stretches as air takes up space in the balloon. Because air takes up space, it is matter.

Look at this kitchen. Everything in the kitchen is matter.

How can you talk about matter? You can measure it. You can tell how big or small it is. You can tell how heavy it is.

You can also use your senses to describe matter. Your senses help you see, feel, taste, smell, and hear things. If you could feel the melon, how would you describe it? You might say it is soft. If you could taste it, you might say it is sweet. How else could you describe a melon?

You have just described the melon's physical properties. **Physical properties** are things about matter that can be measured or found by using your senses. Size, shape, color, texture, hardness, flavor, and temperature are some physical properties.

The melon is soft and sweet.

1. List the physical properties for each category.

   Physical properties that can be measured

   a. _____

   b. _____

   Physical properties that can be found by using the senses

   a. _____

   b. _____

   c. _____

   d. _____

   e. _____

   f. _____

2. What is matter made of?

_____

3. Compare atoms in matter to bricks in a brick wall.

_____

_____

_____

4. Can atoms be seen? Explain your answer.

_____

_____

_____

Atoms

Look at the photo of the boy with the toy animal. The toy is made up of small blocks. When the blocks are put together, they form the toy that you see.

What is matter made of? Like the toy, matter is made of smaller parts. The tiny parts that make up matter are called atoms (AT uhms). An **atom** is the smallest part of some kinds of matter that has the properties of that kind of matter. Atoms are too small to be seen without using special tools.

Every object in your classroom is made of atoms. Books, desks, water, you, and all your classmates are made of atoms.

The metal that makes up these copper objects is matter. Like all matter, it is made up of atoms. The atoms are very, very small. You have to use a strong tool called a microscope to see them.

Because atoms are so tiny, it takes a lot of them to make up one object. There are more atoms in one grain of sand than there are people on Earth!

Copper atoms make up all of these objects.

5. What strong tool do people use to see atoms?

_____

6. What kind of atoms make up all objects that are made of iron?

_____

7. Look at the photos. (Circle) any physical changes being made.

8. (Circle) the examples of a physical change.
   a. cutting hair
   b. mixing lettuce and tomato
   c. blowing up a balloon
   d. peeling an apple

Physical Changes

How do you make a paper airplane? You fold a piece of paper in a set way. This changes the shape of the paper. This is a physical change.

A **physical change** is a change in the size, shape, or form of matter. Physical changes do not change the makeup of the matter. In other words, the matter looks different, but it is still the same kind of matter.

You make many physical changes while folding paper.

You make many physical changes while molding clay.

You make physical changes to matter every day. Sharpen a pencil. Tie your shoes. Push clay into a new shape. These are all physical changes.

Mixing celery into tuna fish is another physical change. You can still taste both the celery and the tuna. Mixing things does not change the celery or the tuna into new kinds of matter. They are still celery and tuna, but now they are mixed together.

MAIN IDEA AND DETAILS

Give two examples of a physical change.

Summary Everything around you is made of matter. Matter is anything that has mass and takes up space. Matter has physical properties such as size, shape, and color. All matter is made up of tiny atoms.

A physical change is a change in size, shape, or form of matter. What kind of physical change is the girl on page 123 making?

_____

_____

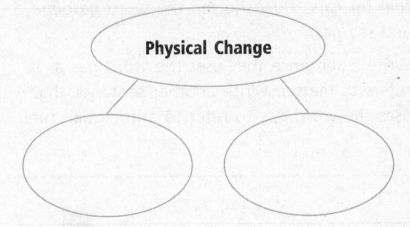

Main Ideas and Details Give two examples of a physical change.

Physical Change

VOCABULARY

gas Matter that has no definite shape and no definite volume. *(noun)*

liquid Matter that takes the shape of its container and has a definite volume. *(noun)*

solid Matter that has a definite shape and a definite volume. *(noun)*

VOCABULARY SKILL: Multiple-Meaning Words

Read the definition of *gas*. This word is sometimes used when people mean *gasoline*, or fuel for cars. They shorten the word *gasoline* and say *gas*.

Write a sentence that uses the word *gas* as it refers to matter. Write another sentence that uses the word *gas* to refer to automobile fuel.

_____

_____

2 What Are the Forms of Matter?

There are three different forms of matter. They are solid, liquid, and gas. Each form has its own physical properties.

Classifying Matter

Matter can be grouped by its physical properties. Look at the water in the glass. The glass and the water are both matter. How would you describe them?

The glass and the water are both matter.

1.e. Students know solid, liquid, and gas are three forms of matter.

Look at this sink. It is made of matter. So is the water that pours into the sink and the air around it. The sink, water, and air are all matter, but they are in different forms.

The forms of matter are solid, liquid, and gas. The sink is a solid. The water is a liquid. The air is a gas. We use physical properties to tell about the form of matter.

The sink, water, and air are different forms of matter.

1. What are the three forms of matter?

   a. _____

   b. _____

   c. _____

2. Circle the liquid matter on these pages.

3. Look at the photo of the boy. For each state of matter, write an example that is in the photo.

   a. solid: _____

   b. liquid: _____

   c. gas: _____

4. Describe a solid.

a. _____

b. _____

5. List the solid objects shown on these pages.

a. _____

b. _____

c. _____

d. _____

e. _____

Solids

A **solid** is matter that has a set shape and takes up a set amount of space.

Look at these pictures. They are all solids. They take up a set amount of space. The CD is always the same shape. It will take up the same space tomorrow that it takes up today.

Solids can be almost any texture, color, weight, or shape.

Matter is made up of many little parts, or particles. In a solid, these particles are very close together. Even though you cannot see them, the particles are moving back and forth in place. They are right next to each other, so they do not have room to move out of their spot. That is why a solid keeps its shape and size.

The particles in a solid are very close together, so they do not have room to slide past each other. This gives solids a set shape.

6. Compare and contrast the physical properties of the CD and the socks.

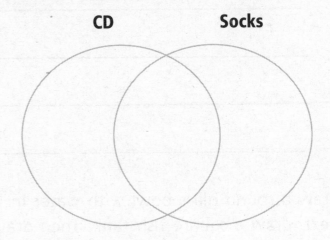

CD   Socks

7. Mattter is made up of particles. Circle the sentence below that correctly tells about particles in a solid.

Particles in a solid have room to slide past each other.

Particles in a solid move about freely.

Particles in a solid are very close together.

8. Describe a liquid.

a. _____

_____

b. _____

_____

9. Draw a round glass bowl with water in it. Next, draw a square fish tank. Then draw what will happen to the shape of the water if you were to pour it into the square fish tank.

Liquids

Put a rock in a glass. The rock's shape does not change when it is put in the glass. A rock is a solid.

Now take the rock out and fill the glass with water. The water takes the shape of the glass. Pour the water into a bowl. The shape of the water changes to match the shape of the bowl.

Water is a liquid. A **liquid** is matter that takes the shape of the thing it is in. But a liquid takes up the same amount of space, even when its shape changes.

Water is a liquid, so it takes the shape of the thing it is in. The same amount of water is in each glass, but it takes a different shape in each one.

Like solids, liquids are made up of particles. The particles are not as close together in a liquid as they are in a solid. There is room for them to move past each other. Because of this, a liquid can flow and change shape.

The particles in a liquid have room to slide past each other. This lets a liquid change shape.

10. (Circle) the sentence below that correctly tells about particles in a liquid.

Particles in a liquid have room to slide past one another.

Particles in a liquid move about freely.

Particles in a liquid are very close together.

11. Draw the particles in a liquid.

129

12. List the properties of a gas.

a. _____

_____

b. _____

_____

c. _____

_____

13. Circle the sentence below that correctly tells about particles in a gas.

Particles in a gas have room to slide past one another.

Particles in a gas move about freely.

Particles in a gas are very close together.

The particles in a gas move about freely. This lets a gas change size and shape.

Gases

Blow air out of your mouth. Air is a gas. It will spread out and mix with other gases in the room. The air in the room does not stay in one corner. It spreads out and moves around. The air takes on the shape and size of the room.

A **gas** is matter that has no set shape and can take up different amounts of space. A gas spreads out to fill the thing it is in. You cannot see most gases.

Like solids and liquids, gases are made up of particles. In a gas, the particles are far away from each other. They have room to move around and spread out to fill their container.

Things to remember about the three forms of matter:

- A solid has a set shape and a set size.
- A liquid has a set size, but takes on the shape of the thing it is in.
- A gas takes on the shape and size of the thing it is in.

Point out the three forms of matter in this picture. (Remember, you cannot always see a gas, but it is still there!)

Summary There are three forms of matter: solid, liquid, and gas. Each state has its own physical properties. Label each picture with the word *solid*, *liquid*, or *gas*.

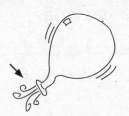  

_____ _____ _____

 Classify What are the three forms of matter? Give an example of each.

Form of Matter	Example
a. _____	
b. _____	
c. _____	

CLASSIFY

What are the three forms of matter? Give an example of each.

VOCABULARY

condense To change form from a gas to a liquid. *(verb)*

evaporate To change form from a liquid to a gas. *(verb)*

freeze To change form from a liquid to a solid. *(verb)*

melt To change form from a solid to a liquid. *(verb)*

thermal energy The energy of moving particles in all matter. *(noun)*

VOCABULARY SKILL: Antonyms

Antonyms are words that have opposite meanings, such as up and down. The words *condense* and *evaporate* are opposites. What other two vocabulary words listed above are opposites?

_____ _____

1.e. Students know solid, liquid, and gas are three forms of matter.
1.f. Students know evaporation and melting are changes caused by heating.

3 How Does Heat Change Matter?

Adding and taking away heat can change matter.

Heating Matter

You learned that all matter is made up of tiny particles that are always moving. Particles in solids move back and forth in one place. Particles in liquids slide past each other. Particles in gases move around freely.

The energy of moving particles in all matter is called **thermal energy** (THUR muhl EHN ur jee). Adding or taking away thermal energy can change matter.

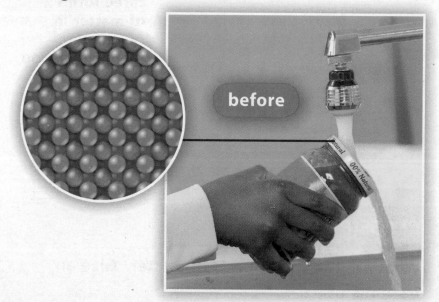

before

Imagine you are trying to open a jar, but the lid is stuck. How can you get it open? You may want to run it under hot water. How does this help you open the jar?

When you run something under hot water, you are adding heat. When you add heat to matter, you are adding thermal energy.

By running hot water over the jar lid, you are adding heat to the lid. This makes the particles in the jar lid move faster and farther apart. The expanded lid is easier to turn.

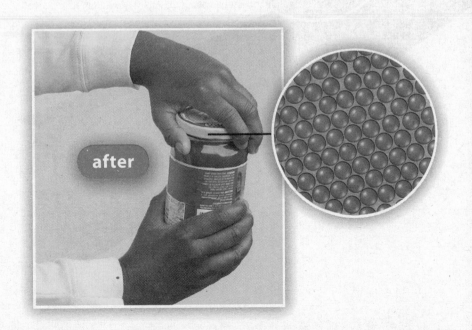

after

1. List two ways to change matter.

   a. _____

   b. _____

2. What is thermal energy?

   _____

   _____

I Wonder . . . You are trying to open a jar. The lid is on too tight to turn. How does adding heat help you? What would be the best way to get the jar open?

_____

_____

_____

_____

_____

3. Fill in the blank.

A solid can change into a liquid when

_____ is added.

4. What physical change occurs when a solid melts?

_____

_____

5. Look at the picture. Tell what happened to the ice cubes and why it happened.

_____

_____

Melting

Heat can even turn a solid into a liquid! If thermal energy is added to the particles in a solid, they slide past each other. The solid does not have a set shape any more. Now it flows and takes on the shape of the thing it is in. It is a liquid!

solid iron

To change from a solid to a liquid is to **melt**. If you add enough thermal energy to a solid, you can make it melt into a liquid.

Melting is a physical change. Melted iron has different physical properties from solid iron. But both solid and liquid iron are made of the same particles of matter.

liquid iron

Add thermal energy to solid iron. It turns into liquid iron!

6. Tell what happens to the particles in iron as it melts.

The bar of iron is a _____.

Then enough _____ is added.

The solid iron _____.

It changes form and becomes _____ iron.

7. Fill in the blanks.

   a. Heat is added. A solid becomes a

      _____.

   b. Then more heat is added. The

      _____ becomes a

      _____.

8. What happens when a liquid evaporates?

_____

I Wonder . . . A girl gets out of a swimming pool on a sunny day. She leaves wet footprints on the concrete. Later the footprints are gone. What happened to the footprints? What do you think?

_____

_____

_____

_____

Evaporation

   Adding thermal energy to a solid makes it melt. It becomes a liquid. What happens if you keep adding thermal energy to the liquid?

   Add thermal energy to a liquid. The particles in the liquid will mover faster and farther apart. They will move so fast and so far apart that the liquid turns into a gas.

   To change from a liquid to a gas is to **evaporate** (ih VAP uh rayt). If you add enough thermal energy to a liquid, you can make it evaporate as a gas.

Hang wet clothes outside to dry. Heat from the Sun will turn the liquid water into a gas. The water will evaporate, leaving the clothes dry.

Like melting, evaporation is a physical change. Water as a liquid has different physical properties than it does as a gas. But they are both made of the same particles of matter.

As the liquid water evaporates, water particles go into the air as a gas.

9. What happens to the water in wet clothes as they dry?

_____

_____

10. Read about the weather on Monday and Tuesday. On which day will the clothes dry faster? Circle that day. Then explain why.

a. Monday it is cool and cloudy.

b. Tuesday it is warm and sunny.

_____

_____

_____

Summary When matter is heated or cooled it can change form. Complete the chart to tell how matter can change form.

Form of Matter	Heat is	What Happens
liquid	taken away	liquid freezes and changes to solid
gas		gas condenses and changes to liquid
liquid	added	
solid		solid melts and changes to liquid

 Sequence What must be added to a solid before it will melt?

_____

_____

Cooling Matter

Taking away thermal energy changes matter, too. When you take away thermal energy, you are cooling matter. The particles slow down and move closer together. Take away enough thermal energy and the matter will change form.

If a gas is cooled, the particles slow down and move together. The matter **condenses**, or changes from a gas to a liquid.

If a liquid is cooled, the particles slow down until they can only move in place. The matter **freezes**, or changes from a liquid to a solid.

In summer, this lake is liquid. In winter, the water freezes into solid ice.

SEQUENCE

What must be added to a solid before it will melt?

atom (AT uhm) The smallest particle of some kinds of matter that has the properties of that kind of matter.

átomo La partícula más pequeña de ciertos tipos de materia que tiene las mismas propiedades que ese tipo de materia.

condense (kuhn DEHNS) To change form from a gas to a liquid.

condensar Cambiar de forma gaseosa a líquida.

evaporate (ih VAP uh rayt) To change form from a liquid to a gas.

evaporar Cambiar de forma líquida a gaseosa.

freeze (freez) To change form from a liquid to a solid.

congelar Cambiar de forma líquida a sólida.

gas (gas) Matter that has no definite shape and no definite volume.

gas Materia que no tiene forma o volumen definidos.

Group two or more of the words on the page and explain why they go together.

Fill in the diagram to tell about liquids.

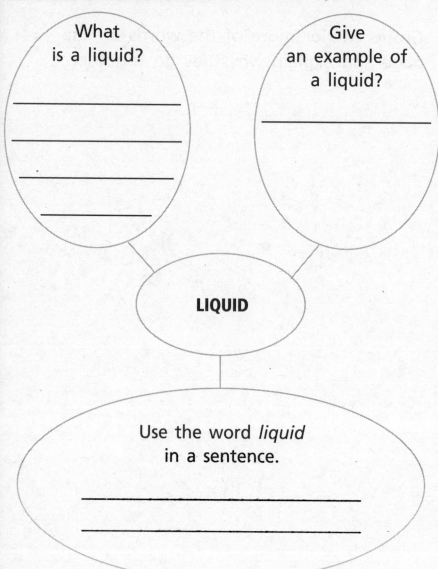

What is a liquid?

_____

_____

_____

Give an example of a liquid?

_____

LIQUID

Use the word *liquid* in a sentence.

_____

_____

Glossary

liquid (LIHK wihd) Matter that takes the shape of its container and has a definite volume.

líquido Materia que toma la forma de su recipiente y que tiene volumen definido.

matter (MAT uhr) Anything that has mass and takes up space. Mass is the amount of matter in an object.

materia Cualquier cosa que tiene masa y ocupa espacio. Masa es la cantidad de material que hay en un objeto.

melt (mehlt) To change form from a solid to a liquid.

derretir Cambiar de forma sólida a líquida.

physical change (FIHZ ih kuhl chaynj) A change in size, shape, or form of matter.

cambio físico Cambio de tamaño, apariencia o forma de la materia.

Glossary

physical property (FIHZ ih kuhl PRAHP uhrtee) A trait of matter that can be measured or observed with the senses.

propiedad física Rasgo de la materia que se puede medir u observar mediante los sentidos.

solid (SAHL ihd) Matter that has a definite shape and a definite volume.

sólido Materia que tiene forma y volumen definidos.

thermal energy (THUHR muhl EHN uhr jee) The energy of moving particles in all matter.

energía térmica Energía de las partículas en movimiento que existen en la materia.

 Visit www.eduplace.com to play puzzles and word games.

Find the word in the glossary that is the same in English and Spanish. (Circle) that word.

141

Chapter Review

WHAT DID YOU LEARN?

Vocabulary

❶ (Circle) the correct answer.

Comprehension

❷ _____

_____

❸ _____

_____

❹ _____

_____

Critical Thinking

❺ _____

Responding

Think About What You Have Read

Vocabulary

❶ The energy of moving particles in all matter is _____.

   A) matter

   B) atom

   C) physical property

   D) thermal energy

Comprehension

❷ What is all matter made of?

❸ How are the particles in a gas spaced?

❹ What two changes of form can occur when thermal energy is added to matter?

Critical Thinking

❺ You find a clear substance that has a definite shape. What form of matter is the substance?

WHAT DO YOU KNOW?

List one fact about each of these topics:

a. Elements _____

_____

_____

_____

b. Chemical Change _____

_____

_____

_____

Chemical Changes

Contents

1 What Are Elements? 146

2 What Is a Chemical Change
in Matter? 153

Glossary 160

WHAT DO YOU WANT TO KNOW?
Skim the pictures and headings in this chapter. Then write a question that you have about each of these topics:

a. Elements _____

_____

_____

_____

b. Chemical changes in matter _____

_____

_____

_____

145

VOCABULARY

compound A substance made of two or more elements that are joined together. *(noun)*

element A pure form of matter in which all of the atoms are the same kind. *(noun)*

mixture Matter made up of two or more substances that are physically combined, or mixed. *(noun)*

periodic table An arrangement of all the elements that gives information about their atoms and properties. *(noun)*

VOCABULARY SKILL: Word Origins

The word *element* comes from the Latin word *elementem*. This word suggests that something is "simple," or "basic." Use the vocabulary term *element* in a sentence.

_____

_____

1.h. Students know all matter is made of particles called atoms that are too small to see.

1.i. Students know people once thought that all matter was made of earth, wind, fire, and water. Scientists have found more than 100 different atoms, which are shown on the periodic table of the elements.

1 What Are Elements?

All matter is made up of one or more kinds of matter called elements. In an element, all of the atoms are the same kind.

Types of Atoms

You may have heard of gold, silver, copper, carbon, or oxygen. They are all elements.

An **element** is a pure kind of matter. Pure means not mixed with other things.

Gold is an element. All of the atoms in a nugget of gold are the same.

In an element, all of the atoms are the same kind. That means an element is the same all the way through. Scientists know of more than 100 different elements.

Elements are the building blocks of all matter because all matter is made up of one or more elements.

Each element has its own kind of atom. Silver is an element. A pure silver ring is made up only of silver atoms. Atoms of silver are different from atoms of any other element.

1. An _____ is a pure kind of matter.

2. List three elements.

   a. _____

   b. _____

   c. _____

3. Look at the photos. (Circle) a gold nugget.

4. Complete each sentence.

   a. A gold nugget is made of one kind of _____.

   b. Gold is a pure kind of matter called a/an _____.

5. Why are elements called building blocks?

   _____

   _____

147

6. Complete each sentence to tell about the periodic table.

a. Scientists group all of the _____ in the periodic table.

b. The way elements are placed in the periodic table tells about their

_____ and their _____.

c. Each box shows the _____ and

_____ for one element.

7. Look at the periodic table. Write the symbol for each element.

a. gold _____

b. silver _____

c. carbon _____

d. copper _____

e. oxygen _____

148

Arranging Elements

Scientists group all of the elements in a chart. The chart is called the periodic table of the elements. In the **periodic table**, elements are placed in a way that tells about their atoms and properties.

Look at the periodic table. Each box shows the name and symbol for one element.

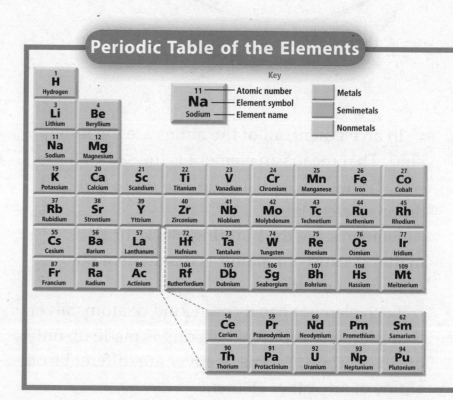

Periodic Table of the Elements

You can learn about an element by where it is placed in the periodic table. Find gold and silver in the table. They are near each other. That is because they have a lot of the same properties.

Gold and silver are both heavy and shiny. They can be shaped. They do not rust or burn. Other elements near gold and silver in the periodic table have many of the same properties.

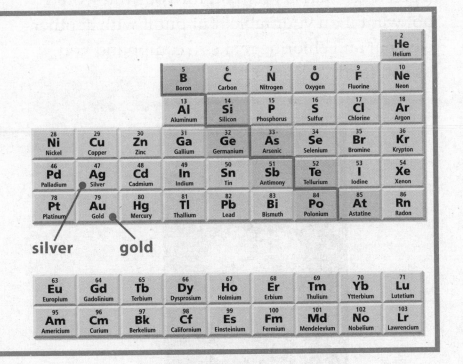

8. How do scientists determine the placement of elements on the periodic table?

_____

_____

9. List three reasons for placing gold and silver near each other on the periodic table.

a. _____

b. _____

c. _____

I Wonder . . . The element platinum, symbol Pt, is placed near gold on the periodic table. What properties might gold and platinum share?

_____

_____

10. Something made up of two or more elements joined together is called a

_____.

11. Fill in the blanks.

_____ + element = _____

Compounds

Some things we use every day, such as water, sugar, and salt, are not on the periodic table. Why? Because they are not elements. They are made up of elements. Something made up of two or more elements joined together is called a **compound**.

Compounds can have very different properties than the elements in them. Table salt is a compound made from the element chlorine, a green gas that is very bad for you. You would not want it on your table! But put it with another element and chlorine makes a compound you use on food.

table salt

SUGAR
This common compound is fuel that plants and animals use for energy.

SILICON DIOXIDE
Glass is made from the compound silicon dioxide, which is found in common sand.

CITRIC ACID
This common compound in orange juice makes foods taste sour.

WATER
This common compound is made of the gases hydrogen and oxygen.

12. Read the clue. Tell the compound it describes.

Clue	Compound
This compound is fuel that plants and animals use for energy.	_____
This compound, found in sand, is used to make glass.	_____
This compound, which you sprinkle on food, contains the element chlorine.	_____
This compound in orange juice makes foods taste sour.	_____
This compound, which you drink, is made of the gases hydrogen and oxygen.	_____

151

Summary All matter is made up of one or more elements. In an element, all of the atoms are of the same kind. Compounds are made of two or more kinds of atoms joined together forming a new kind of matter. A compound has properties that are different from the elements it is made of. A mixture is made of two or more kinds of matter that are mixed together. The properties of the things in a mixture remain the same after they are mixed.

Name a mixture and list all of its parts.

_____

_____

Compare and Contrast How are mixtures and compounds different?

Mixtures	Compounds

made
up of more
than one kind
of matter

Mixtures

Most kinds of matter are mixtures. A **mixture** is matter made up of two or more things that are put together, or mixed.

In a compound, the elements mix to make something new with new properties. In a mixture, the things that are mixed together keep their own properties. They are not joined together.

Look at the nachos. They are a mixture of chips, beans, olives, tomatoes, and cheese. The properties of each of these things do not change when they are mixed together. The beans are still beans.

Nachos are a mixture.

COMPARE AND CONTRAST

How are mixtures and compounds different?

What Is a Chemical Change in Matter?

You have learned about physical changes, such as folding paper and shaping clay. Now you will learn about chemical changes. A chemical change makes a new compound with different properties.

Chemical Reactions

Look at the silver candleholder before and after it was cleaned. Before cleaning, the silver is dull and dark. After cleaning, the silver is bright and shiny.

What made the silver dull and dark? Silver reacts with sulfur, an element in air. When sulfur contacts the silver, it makes a new compound with different properties. Silver is bright and shiny, but the new compound is dull and dark.

Before   After

 1.g. Students know that when two or more substances are combined, a new substance may form that is different from the original materials.

VOCABULARY

chemical change A change in matter in which one or more new kinds of matter form. *(noun)*

chemical property A property that describes how matter can react with other kinds of matter. *(noun)*

VOCABULARY SKILL: Word Context

Both vocabulary terms contain the word *chemical*. Read both definitions. How are they related?

_____

_____

1. What is a chemical property?

_____

_____

2. List three chemical properties of matter.

a. _____

b. _____

c. _____

3. What happens during a chemical change?

_____

_____

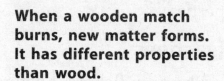

When a wooden match burns, new matter forms. It has different properties than wood.

Silver reacts with sulfur. That is a chemical (KEHM ih kuhl) property of silver. A **chemical property** tells how one kind of matter reacts with other kinds of matter. Being able to burn, rust, and explode are all chemical properties.

A match is made of wood, and wood can burn. Look at the match before and after it burned. Burning changed the physical and chemical properties of the wood.

The burned match is not wood. It is a different kind of matter. A chemical change has happened. A **chemical change** is a change in matter in which one or more new kinds of matter form. The matter that changes and the new matter that forms have different properties.

Physical and Chemical Changes

When there is a physical change in matter, no new matter forms. Paper that is folded is still paper. It has the same properties. It may look different, but the atoms in it have not changed.

When matter goes through a chemical change, a new kind of matter always forms. You start with one kind of matter and end up with another kind of matter. Paper that is burned makes a powder called ash. Ash and paper look different and have different physical properties.

folded paper

burned paper

4. Fill in the blanks to compare two kinds of changes in matter.

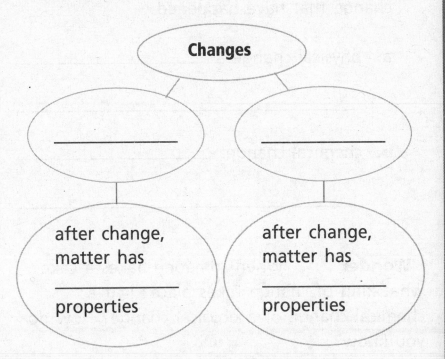

Changes

_____

_____

after change, matter has

_____

properties

after change, matter has

_____

properties

5. For each example, write what kind of change in matter it is.

a. paper is folded: _____

b. paper is burned: _____

6. Look at the photo of the marshmallow. Tell one chemical change and one physical change that have happened.

a. physical change: _____

_____

b. chemical change: _____

_____

I Wonder . . . When someone bakes a cake, what kind of change takes place? Is it a chemical change or a physical change? How do you know?

_____

_____

_____

_____

Have you ever toasted a marshmallow? You can see both physical and chemical changes. First, the marshmallow starts to melt. This is a physical change.

As you keep toasting it, sugar in the marshmallow changes into the element carbon. You can see the carbon as a dark color on the outside of the marshmallow. The marshmallow has gone through both physical and chemical changes.

The carbon on this toasted marshmallow shows that it went through a chemical change.

Comparing Changes in Matter

Physical Changes	Chemical Changes
 Breaking up a sugar cube does not change the kind of matter. Tiny pieces of sugar are still sugar.	 **Caramel is burned sugar. Heat changes sugar into water and carbon.**
 **Folding paper does not change the atoms in the paper. Folded paper is still paper.**	**When paper burns, it turns into ash. Ash is a new kind of matter.**
 **Copper can be bent. Bending the copper does not change the atoms.**	 **When copper and wet air combine, they make a green coating. This green coating is not copper.**

7. Complete the chart. Tell a physical and a chemical change you could make to each object.

Kind of Matter	Physical Change	Chemical Change
sugar cube	_____	_____
paper	_____	_____
copper	_____	_____

8. When paper burns, it turns to ash. When sugar burns, it changes to caramel, which is water and carbon. What do ash, water, and carbon have in common?

_____

_____

9. What chemical changes happen when you eat food?

_____

_____

_____

10. Look at the photo. How did the pancakes change as they cooked?

_____

_____

_____

11. 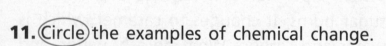 the examples of chemical change.

   a. food cooking

   b. water freezing

   c. a match burning

   d. iron rusting

Useful Chemical Changes

Chemical changes happen every day. Many happen in your body. When you eat, chemical changes turn food into things your body uses to grow.

Cooking food also causes chemical changes. When you cook pancake batter, it comes out as pancakes. The cooked pancakes have different properties than the batter.

Heating clay causes a chemical change. After heating, the vase is strong and shiny. It is waterproof.

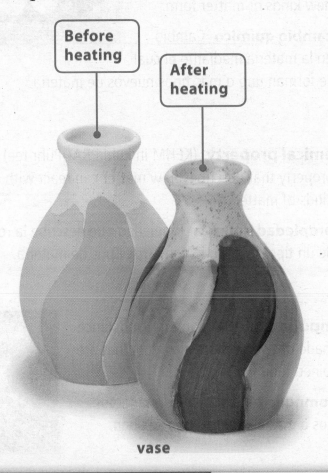

Before heating

After heating

vase

Describe the changes that occur when you toast a marshmallow.

Summary In a chemical change, new matter forms that has different properties from the original matter. Describe three useful chemical changes?

a. _____

b. _____

c. _____

Sequence Describe the changes that occur when you toast a marshmallow.

The marshmallow is _____.

↓

The marshmallow begins to _____, which is a _____ change.

↓

The sugar in the marshmallow starts to burn, which is a _____ change.

(Circle) all of the vocabulary terms that are made up of two words. Write these terms on the lines below.

_____

_____

_____

chemical change (KEHM ih kuhl chaynj) A change in matter in which one or more new kinds of matter form.

cambio químico Cambio en la materia mediante el cual se forman uno o más tipos nuevos de materia.

chemical property (KEHM ih kuhl PRAHPuhr tee) A property that describes how matter can react with other kinds of matter.

propiedad química Propiedad que describe la reacción de un tipo de materia con otros tipos de materia.

compound (KAHM pound) A substance made of two or more elements that are joined together.

compuesto Sustancia formada por dos o más elementos que se unen.

Glossary

element (EHL ih mehnt) A pure form
of matter in which all of the
atoms are the same kind.

elemento Forma pura de materia
cuyos átomos son todos del mismo tipo.

mixture (MIHKS chur) Matter
made up of two or more
substances that are physically
combined, or mixed.

mezcla Materia en la que se
combinan o mezclan
físicamente dos o más sustancias.

periodic table (PEER ee ahd ik
TAY buhl) An arrangement of all
the elements that gives
information about their atoms
and properties.

tabla periódica Disposición de
todos los elementos, con
información sobre sus átomos
y propiedades.

Visit www.eduplace.com to play puzzles
and word games.

Find the English words that are like these
Spanish words. List those words in the chart.

Spanish	English
elemento	
periódica	
tabla	

Chapter Review

WHAT DID YOU LEARN?

Vocabulary

❶ (Circle) the correct answer.

Comprehension

❷ _____

_____

❸ _____

_____

❹ _____

_____

Critical Thinking

❺ _____

162

Responding

Think About What You Have Read

Vocabulary

❶ All of the atoms are of the same kind in a/an _____.

  A) chemical change

  B) compound

  C) element

  D) mixture

Comprehension

❷ What is the periodic table?

❸ A compound is made up of _____.

❹ What happens during a chemical change?

Critical Thinking

❺ You make a salad out of lettuce, tomatoes, and carrots. Would you classify the salad as a compound or a mixture?

WHAT DO YOU KNOW?
List one fact about each of these topics:

a. Energy _____

_____

_____

b. Waves _____

_____

_____

c. Electrical Energy _____

_____

_____

164

Forms of Energy

Contents

1 What Is Energy? 166

2 How Is Energy Converted? 169

3 What Are Waves? 173

4 What Is Electrical Energy? 176

Glossary 180

WHAT DO YOU WANT TO KNOW?

Skim the pictures and headings in this chapter. List one thing you want to find out about each of these topics:

a. Energy _____

_____

b. How energy is converted _____

_____

c. Waves _____

_____

d. Electrical Energy _____

_____

Lesson Preview

VOCABULARY

energy The ability to cause matter to change or move. *(noun)*

VOCABULARY SKILL: Word Context

Thermal energy is one type of energy that you will learn about in this lesson. Read the definition of *thermal energy* on the next page. Circle the words *heat* and *warm. Thermal* is a word that means "heat."

1.a. Students know energy comes from the Sun to Earth as light.
1.b. Students know there is stored energy in food, fuel, and batteries.
1.d. Students know energy can be carried from one place to another by water waves and sound waves, by electricity, and by moving objects.

166

1 What Is Energy?

Energy is the ability to move or change things. There are many kinds of energy.

Forms of Energy

Energy is the ability to make things move or change matter in other ways. You use energy to ride a bike. A stove uses energy to cook food. Your eyes use energy from the Sun to see. How can energy do all of these things?

There are many kinds, or forms, of energy. Each form of energy changes matter, but in different ways. A bike is matter. The energy you use to ride a bike makes it move.

These children use energy to play a game.

Forms of Energy

Chemical Energy is energy stored in things such as food and batteries.

Light Energy is energy you can see. Earth gets it from the Sun.

Electrical (ih LEHK trih kuhl) **energy** is used to run appliances and other machines.

Mechanical (mih KAN ih kuhl) **energy** is the energy of moving things. It is used to move people and things from place to place.

Sound Energy is energy you can hear. It is used to hear music.

Thermal energy is the energy of tiny moving particles of matter. It is used to heat food and warm homes. Heat is thermal energy moving from one thing to another.

1. Energy is the ability to _____ or _____ things.

2. Complete the chart to show the type of energy described by the clue.

Clue	Type of Energy
Energy used to heat food	
Energy of moving things	
Energy you hear	
Energy stored in food	
Energy used to run machines	
Energy you can see	

Summary Energy is the ability to cause things to move or to cause other changes in matter. There are many forms of energy.

List three things that the chemical energy in food helps you do.

1. _____

2. _____

3. _____

Classify What form of energy does a moving guitar string make?

_____

_____

_____

Useful Chemical Energy

Chemical energy is stored in things such as food, batteries, and gasoline. It can be used in many different ways.

You need the chemical energy in food to live, move, and grow. The food you eat in one day has as much chemical energy as two car batteries!

car battery

car battery

=

CLASSIFY

What form of energy does a moving guitar string make?

How Is Energy Converted?

Machines and living things change stored energy to motion and heat.

Kinetic and Potential Energy

Some energy is in motion, or moving from one place to another. Someone sledding down a hill has energy of motion. Energy of motion is called **kinetic energy** (kuh NEHT ihk EHN ur jee).

Other kinds of energy, such as chemical energy, do not use motion. Chemical energy is stored energy. It has energy based on where it is, or its position. The energy of position is called **potential energy** (puh TEHN shuhl EHN ur jee). Someone standing at the top of a hill has potential energy.

As the boy slides down the hill, he has kinetic energy because of his motion.

VOCABULARY

friction A force that occurs when one object rubs against another object. *(noun)*

kinetic energy The energy of motion. *(noun)*

potential energy The energy of position. *(noun)*

VOCABULARY SKILL: Word Origins

Read the definition of *kinetic energy*. *Kinetic* comes from the Greek word *kinetikos*, which means "moving." Moving objects have kinetic energy. Rewrite the definition of *kinetic energy* to include the word *moving*.

_____

_____

1.a. Students know energy comes from the Sun to Earth as light.
1.b. Students know there is stored energy in food, fuel, and batteries.
1.c. Students know machines and living things change stored energy to motion and heat.

1. Identify each type of energy.

   a. Energy of motion: _____

   b. Energy of position: _____

2. Circle the word that makes each sentence true.

   a. Potential energy can (change, move) to kinetic energy.

   b. When you hold a ball above the ground, the ball has (potential, kinetic) energy because of its position.

   c. A ball that is (rolling, on a high shelf) has kinetic energy.

Storing and Releasing Energy

Energy can change from potential to kinetic. It can also change back from kinetic to potential.

Hold a ball in your hand. The ball has potential energy because of its position. Drop the ball. Now the ball is in motion, so it has kinetic energy.

The ball bounces. As it moves up into the air, it slows down. The ball slows down because its kinetic energy is changing back to potential energy.

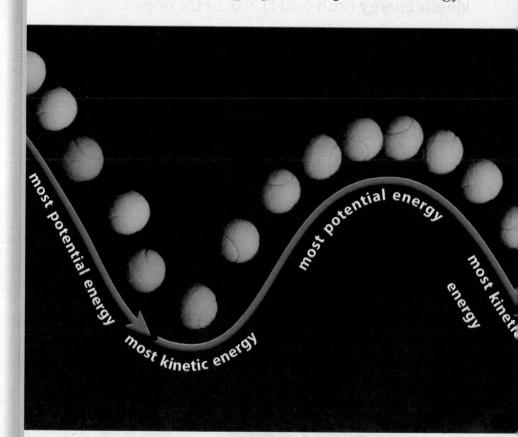

most potential energy

most kinetic energy

most potential energy

most kinetic energy

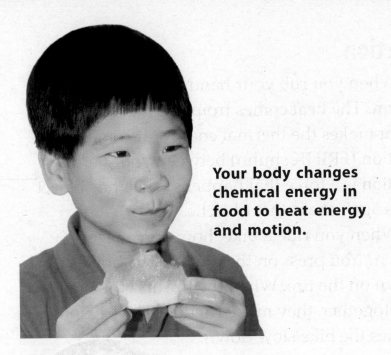

Your body changes chemical energy in food to heat energy and motion.

Changing Forms of Energy

Energy can change from one form to another, too. When you use energy, it almost always changes form. When you turn on a light, electrical energy changes to light energy. When you eat, chemical energy in food changes to mechanical and thermal energy.

Most forms of energy can change to thermal energy. You feel warm when you stand in sunlight. That is because the Sun gives off thermal energy.

Think about a toaster and a hair dryer. How do they work? Like many things in your home, they use electrical energy to make thermal energy.

3. Energy can change from one _____ to another.

4. Tell the energy change that occurs with each action.

Action	Energy Change
Turning on an electric light	_____ changes to light energy.
Eating food	_____ changes to thermal and mechanical energy.
Using a hair dryer	Electrical energy changes to _____.

Summary   Kinetic energy is energy of motion. Potential energy is energy of position. Energy can change from one form to another. Machines and living things change stored energy to motion and heat. Friction is a force caused by objects rubbing together.

What force makes a bike slow down?

_____

Cause and Effect What causes your hands to get warm when you rub them together? Fill in the box to explain what happens.

Cause	Effect
	My hands get warm when I rub them together.

Friction

When you rub your hands together, they get warm. The heat comes from thermal energy. But what makes the thermal energy? It comes from friction (FRIHK shuhn) between your hands. **Friction** is a force that happens when one object rubs against another object.

When you ride a bike, how do you slow down? You press on the brakes. The brakes push down on the tire. When the tire and the brakes rub together, they make friction. The friction makes the bike slow down.

tire

brakes

CAUSE AND EFFECT

What causes your hands to get warm when you rub them together?

What Are Waves?

Waves carry energy from place to place.

How Energy Travels

Rocks fall down the side of a mountain and into the ocean. It's a landslide! The energy of the moving rocks makes waves in the ocean. The waves reach a far-off shore. Water rushes over the land. How did the energy of the landslide move through the water? It moved as waves. A **wave** is a movement that carries energy from one place to another.

All waves have properties you can see. The **crest** is the highest point of the wave. The **trough** (trawf) is the lowest point of the wave. The distance between two crests is the wavelength.

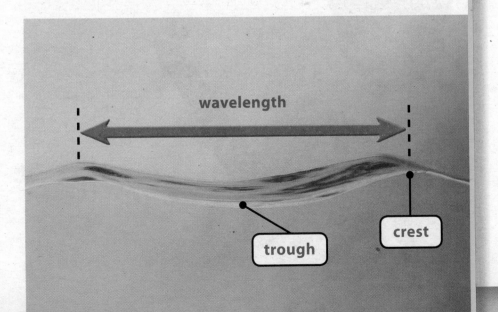

wavelength

trough

crest

VOCABULARY

crest The highest point of a wave. *(noun)*

trough The lowest point of a wave. *(noun)*

vibrate To move back and forth quickly. *(verb)*

wave A movement that carries energy from one place to another. *(noun)*

VOCABULARY SKILL: Decoding

Write the word *trough*. Circle the blend that begins this word *(tr)*. In this word, the letters *-ough* make the same sound as *o-f-f*. Write the word *trough* the way it sounds. Practice saying the word.

_____

 1.d. Students know energy can be carried from one place to another by water waves and sound waves, by electricity, and by moving objects. **173**

1. Waves carry _____ from place to place.

2. a. The highest point of a wave is its _____.

   b. The lowest point of a wave is its _____.

3. How does sound energy move?

   _____

   _____

4. Tell why pulling on a guitar string and then letting it go produces sound waves.

   _____

   _____

   _____

Sound Waves

Waves do not move only in water. Waves can move through air and other things, too.

Sound energy moves in waves. Sound is made when things **vibrate** (VY brayt), or move back and forth quickly.

When you play a guitar, you pull a string. The string moves back and forth very fast. This makes sound waves in the air. The sound waves move out in all directions. You hear the waves as sounds.

Sound Moves Through Matter

You often hear sound waves through the air, which is a gas. But sound waves can also move through liquids. Look at these dolphins. They use sound waves to talk to each other under water.

Sound waves can move through solids, too. Sound waves move through solids faster than they move through liquids. They move through liquids faster than through gases. That means sound waves move faster through a wood door than through air!

dolphins

DRAW CONCLUSIONS

Will a sound wave travel fastest through air, water, or wood?

Summary   Waves carry energy from place to place. Sound is the energy of vibrating matter. Sound waves can travel through liquids, solids, and gases.

How are dolphins able to talk to one another under water?

_____

_____

Draw Conclusions   Will a sound wave travel fastest through air, water, or wood?

_____

_____

VOCABULARY

electric circuit A path through which electric current can flow. *(noun)*

electric current The flow of charged particles. *(noun)*

VOCABULARY SKILL: Word Origins

Read the definition of *electric circuit*. The term *circuit* is from the Latin word *circuitus*, which means "going around." The word *circle* also comes from *circuitus*. How is a circuit like a circle?

_____

_____

1.c. Students know machines and living things change stored energy to motion and heat.

1.d. Students know energy can be carried from one place to another by water waves and sound waves, by electricity, and by moving objects.

4 What Is Electrical Energy?

Electrical energy moves through paths called electric circuits.

Flow of Electric Charges

All matter is made up of small particles. Some particles are charged. This means they are positive or negative. Electrical energy is the energy of charged particles.

Negative particles tend to flow, or move, toward positive particles. This flow of charged particles is an **electric current** (KUR uhnt).

Lamps use electrical energy.

Electric current flows through a path called an **electric circuit** (SUR kiht). A circuit is made up of wires and a source of electricity, such as a battery. If there is a gap in the circuit, the electric current cannot flow.

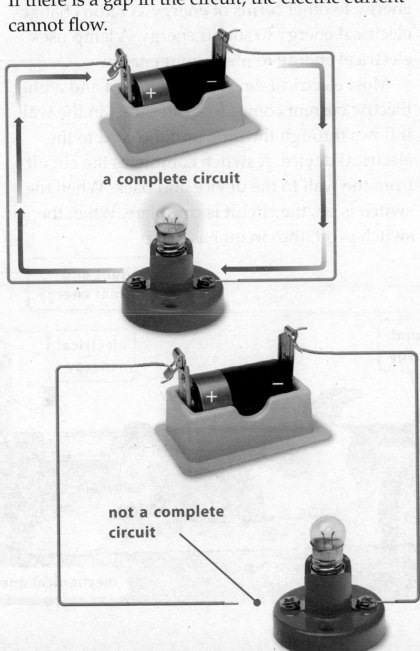

a complete circuit

not a complete circuit

1. What is all matter made up of?

   _____

2. Electrical energy is the energy of

   _____ _____.

3. The flow of charged particles is called

   a/an _____ _____.

4. Electric current flows through a path called

   a/an _____ _____.

I Wonder . . . Why can't an electrical current flow if there is a gap in the circuit?

_____

_____

_____

_____

5. A radio changes _____ energy to

_____ energy.

6. Fill in the missing step to describe the path that an electric current takes as it flows through a lamp.

> Electric current comes from an outlet in the wall.

↓

>

↓

> The current flows back down the cord, through the plug, and into the outlet.

Converting Electrical Energy

Electric current runs many things, called electrical devices. Most of them change electrical energy to other forms of energy. A radio changes electrical energy to sound energy. A lamp uses electrical energy to make light energy.

Most electrical devices have a cord and a plug. Electric current comes from an outlet in the wall. It flows through the plug and the cord to the electrical device. A switch completes the circuit from the wall to the device and back. When the switch is on, the circuit is complete. When the switch is off, the circuit has a gap.

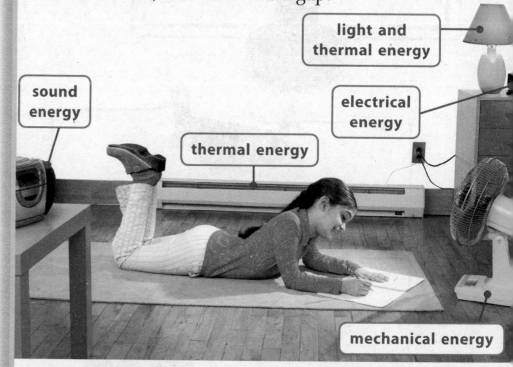

light and thermal energy

sound energy

electrical energy

thermal energy

mechanical energy

Electrical Energy and Your Body

Your body uses electrical energy every day! When you eat food, you get chemical energy. Your body changes the chemical energy into electrical energy. Then it uses that energy to keep your heart beating. It uses it to send messages from your brain to other parts of your body, too.

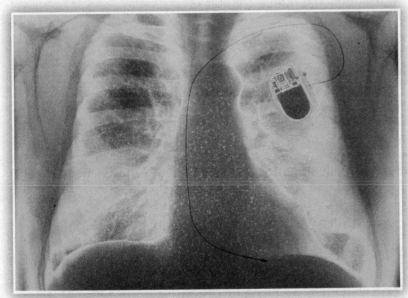

Doctors can put a pacemaker in a heart to help it beat. It runs on electrical energy.

CAUSE AND EFFECT

Why does an electrical device work only when its switch is turned on?

Summary Electrical energy is the energy of charged particles. The flow of charged particles is an electric current. Electric current moves through a path called an electric circuit. For current to flow, the circuit must be complete. Electrical devices change electrical energy to sound, light, heat, or motion.

You get chemical energy from the foods you eat. Your body changes chemical energy into electrical energy. What are two ways in which your body uses electrical energy?

1. _____

2. _____

Cause and Effect Why does an electrical device work only when its switch is turned on?

Cause	Effect
	Electricity can flow through the electrical device and back.

179

Glossary

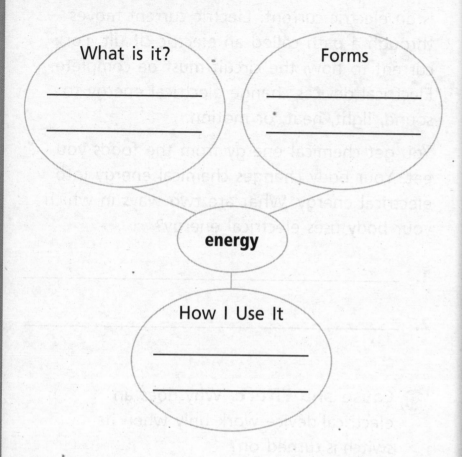

What is it?

_____

_____

Forms

_____

_____

energy

How I Use It

_____

_____

Glossary

crest (krest) The highest point of a wave.

  cresta Punto más alto de una onda.

electric circuit (EE lek trik SUR kiht) A path through which electric current can flow.

  circuito eléctrico Recorrido a través del cual puede circular la corriente eléctrica.

electric current (EE lek trik KUR uhnt) The flow of charged particles.

  corriente eléctrica Flujo de partículas con carga.

energy (EHN ur jee) The ability to cause matter to change or move.

  energía Capacidad que tiene la materia de cambiar o moverse.

friction (FRIHK shuhn) A force that occurs when one object rubs against another object.

  fricción Fuerza que tiene lugar cuando un objeto roza con otro.

Glossary

kinetic energy (kuh NEHT ihk EHN ur jee) The energy of motion.

energía cinética Energía del movimiento.

potential energy (puh TEHN shuhl EHN urjee) The energy of position.

energía potencial Energía de posición.

trough (trawf) The lowest point of a wave.

valle Punto más bajo de una onda.

vibrate (VY brayt) To move back and forth quickly.

vibrar Moverse hacia un lado y otro rápidamente.

wave (wayv) A movement that carries energy from one place to another.

onda Movimiento que lleva energía de un lugar a otro.

 Visit www.eduplace.com to play puzzles and word games.

(Circle) the English words and their meanings for all the glossary words.

Chapter Review

WHAT DID YOU LEARN?

Vocabulary

❶ (Circle) the correct answer.

Comprehension

❷ _____

_____

❸ _____

_____

_____

❹ _____

_____

Critical Thinking

❺ _____

_____

Responding

Think About What You Have Read

Vocabulary

❶ The ability to cause movement or changes in matter is _____.

   A) energy

   B) friction

   C) a trough

   D) a wave

Comprehension

❷ Suppose you are at the top of a hill wearing roller skates. If you convert your potential energy to kinetic energy, what will happen?

❸ How does energy travel from place to place?

❹ What is electrical energy?

Critical Thinking

❺ The Sun is the main source of light energy during the day. What are some sources of light energy you can use at night?

Light

KWL

WHAT DO YOU KNOW?

List one fact about each of these topics:

a. Light _____

_____

_____

b. How light is reflected _____

_____

_____

c. Color _____

_____

_____

Contents

1 What Is Light? 186

2 How Is Light Reflected? 192

3 What Is Color? 196

Glossary 200

WHAT DO YOU WANT TO KNOW?

Skim the pictures and headings in this chapter. List one thing you want to find out about each of these topics:

a. Light _____

_____

_____

b. Reflecting Light _____

_____

_____

c. Color _____

_____

_____

Lesson Preview

VOCABULARY

light A form of energy that you can see. *(noun)*

opaque Not allowing light to pass through. *(adjective)*

shadow An area where light does not strike the ground. *(noun)*

translucent Allows only some light to pass through. *(adjective)*

transparent Lets light pass through. *(adjective)*

VOCABULARY SKILL: Prefixes

The prefix *trans-* means "across." Write the two vocabulary terms that begin with the prefix *trans-*. Circle the prefix in each word.

_____

_____

2.a. Students know sunlight can be blocked to make shadows.
2.d. Students know when light traveling from an object enters the eye, the object is seen.

186

1 What Is Light?

We can see objects because of light. Light moves from the object and into our eyes. Shadows are made when light is blocked.

Energy You Can See

Look around you. What can you see? You can see things because of light. **Light** is a kind of energy. It moves in waves. Light waves move away from their source, or the place where they start.

Most objects do not give off their own light. You can see them because light from another source bounces off of them.

Lights can make night seem like day.

How can you see an object? Light waves hit the object and bounce off it. Then the light waves hit your eyes.

Look at the picture. The boy can see the toys. Light waves from a bulb hit the toys. Some of the light waves bounce from the objects to the boy's eyes. Then he can see them.

The boy sees the objects when light waves bounce from their surfaces to his eyes.

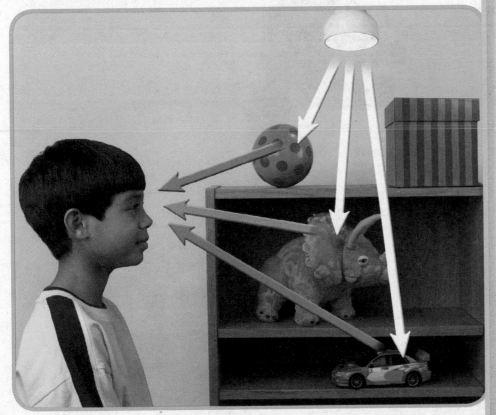

1. Fill in the blanks.

   Light is a kind of _____ that moves

   in _____.

2. Most objects do not give off their own light. Tell how you see them.

   _____

   _____

3. Draw arrows to show how you see the toy and the book. The arrows should show how light travels.

   Toy

   Lamp   My Eye

   Book

187

4. An object that lets light pass through it is a/an _____ object.

5. Draw an arrow to show what happens to light when it strikes a transparent object.

clear glass

light source

Light and Matter

You can see through water, but you cannot see through a rock. Why can you see through some things and not others?

You can see through things that are transparent (trahns PAIR uhnt), such as water and glass. A **transparent** object lets light pass through it. Windows are made of transparent glass so that you can see through them.

transparent

You can partly see through things that are translucent (trahns LOO suhnt), such as frosted glass. A **translucent** object lets some light pass through it, but sends the light in many directions. Objects seen through translucent objects look blurry.

You cannot see through things that are opaque (oh PAYK), such as wood and rock. An **opaque** object does not let light pass through it. Walls are opaque. People are opaque, too. You cannot see through them.

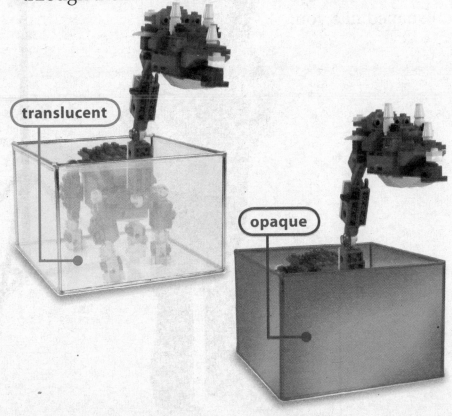

translucent

opaque

6. Draw an arrow to show what happens to light when it hits an opaque object.

light source

wooden door

7. Use *transparent*, *translucent*, or *opaque* to describe each object.

   a. clear window _____

   b. wooden door _____

   c. wall _____

   d. clean water _____

   e. person _____

   f. frosted glass _____

8. What is a shadow?

_____

_____

9. Place an X where the shadow will fall.

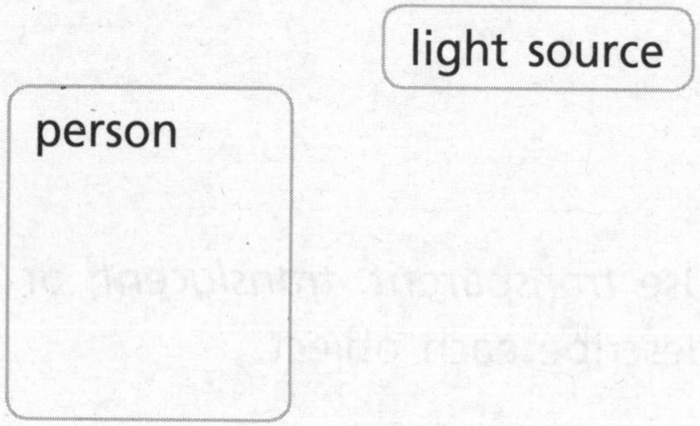

light source

person

I Wonder . . . Are there shadows at night?

_____

_____

_____

_____

Shadows

What happens when light hits an opaque object, such as your body? Some of the light waves hit your body. Your body blocks those light waves. But some of the light goes past your body and hits the ground or a wall.

A **shadow** is made where your body blocks the light. A shadow is a place where light does not strike. Only the light waves that hit your body are blocked, so the shadow is shaped like you.

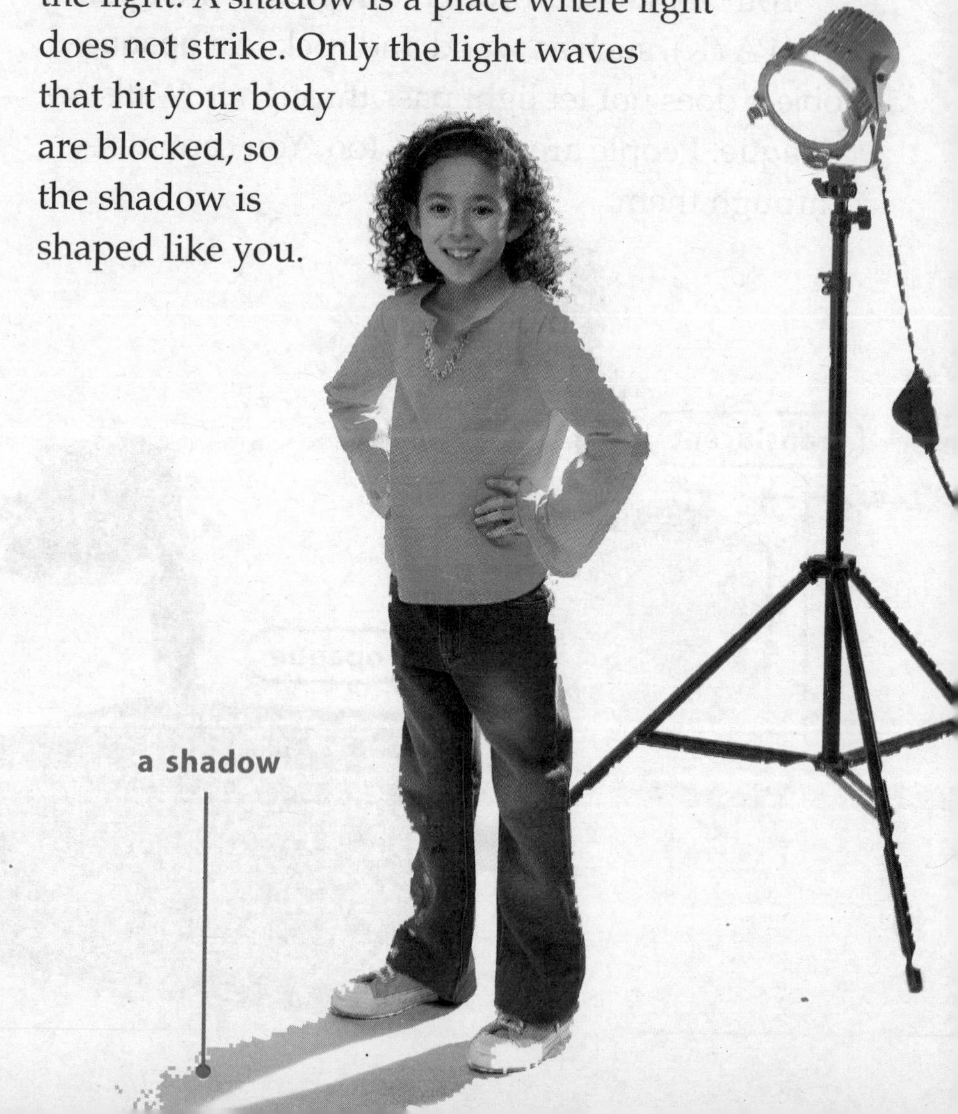

a shadow

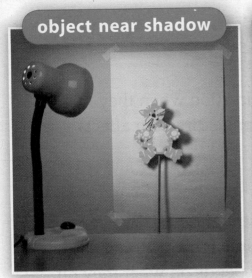
object near shadow

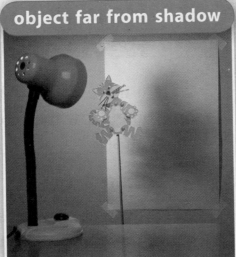
object far from shadow

Sharp Shadows

Look at the shadows in these pictures. In the first picture, the shadow is about the same size as the puppet. The edges are clean and sharp.

In the second picture, the shadow is a lot bigger than the puppet. The edges of the shadow are blurry. What makes the shadows different?

An object that is close to its shadow makes a small, sharp shadow. An object that is far from its shadow makes a large, blurry shadow.

MAIN IDEA

Where should you hold your hands to make a clear, sharp shadow on the wall?

Summary Objects are seen when light traveling from them enters the eye. A shadow forms when light is blocked. List three words used to describe how light passes through materials and explain each term.

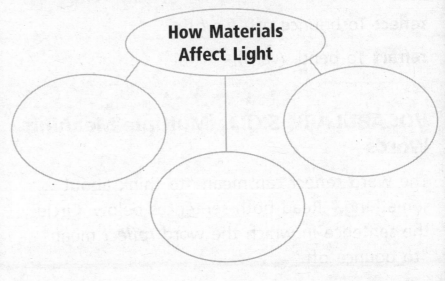

How Materials Affect Light

Main Idea Where should you hold your hands to make a clear, sharp shadow on the wall?

VOCABULARY

lens An object that refracts light. *(noun)*

reflect To bounce off. *(verb)*

refract To bend. *(verb)*

VOCABULARY SKILL: Multiple-Meaning Words

The word *reflect* can mean "to think about something." Read both sentences below. Circle the sentence in which the word *reflect* means "to bounce off."

After reading this lesson, I will reflect on what I learned.

When water is still and smooth, it will reflect light just as a mirror does.

2 How Is Light Reflected?

Light waves change direction when they hit something. How they change direction affects what you see.

Reflection

Light waves move in straight lines. But they change directions when they hit something. How their direction changes depends on what they hit.

Light waves **reflect** (rih FLEHKT), or bounce, off most objects. When light waves hit a mirror, they reflect right back to your eyes. That is why you see yourself.

Light waves can also hit things that are not smooth and shiny like a mirror. Then they bounce back in many directions.

This water is very smooth. It reflects light like a mirror.

2.b. Students know mirrors and other surfaces reflect light.
2.d. Students know when light traveling from an object enters the eye, the object is seen.

Refraction

Look at the pencil. Is it broken? No, but the way light hits it makes it look broken.

The path of light waves changes when it hits some things, such as air or water. Light waves refract (rih FRAKT) when they move from air to water. To **refract** is to bend. Refracted light makes things look bent or broken. The pencil looks as if it is broken because light bends when it moves from water to air.

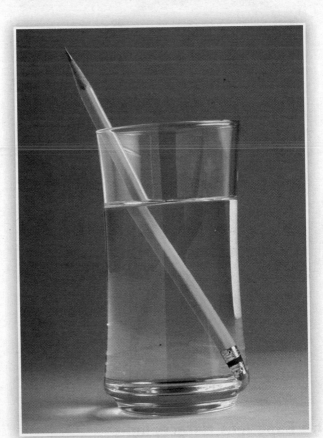

This pencil looks broken because of refraction.

1. (Circle) the term that correctly completes each sentence about how light waves change direction

   a. When light waves move from air to water they (bounce, bend).

   b. When light waves strike a mirror they (bounce, bend) back to your eyes.

2. Use the words *reflect* and *refract* to label each picture.

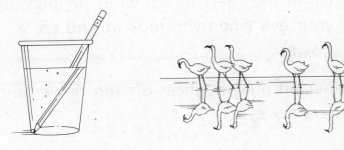

_____   _____

193

3. Fill in the blanks.

a. A lens is an object that _____ light.

b. Objects look bigger when viewed with a

_____.

c. The lens in eyeglasses is made of

_____ glass.

4. Fill in the chart to tell what happens in your eye when you look at and see a flower.

Reflected light bounces off the flower and enters my eye.

↓

The lens of my eye _____ the light. The image is _____ in my eye.

↓

My brain _____ the image of the flower so that I can see it correctly.

A **lens** is an object that refracts light. A lens is made of glass. Glass refracts light. The lens in eyeglasses is curved to bend light. This helps people see better.

A hand lens is made of glass. It is curved, too. It refracts light to make objects look bigger.

This hand lens refracts light.

The Human Eye

Each of your eyes has a lens, too. The lens is near the front of your eye.

When you look at an object, reflected light goes into your eye. The lens bends the light. Your eye makes an image of the object. The image is upside down! Your brain "flips" the image so that you can see it correctly.

Human Eye

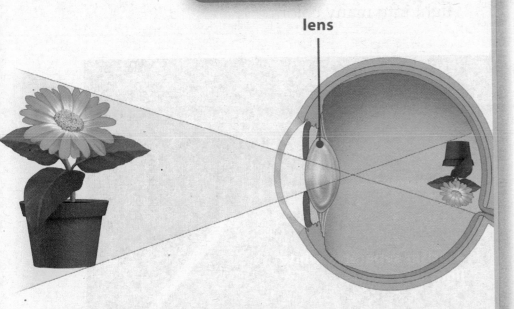

lens

Summary   Light waves change direction, depending on the kind of surface they strike. Smooth shiny surfaces reflect light. Light can refract, or bend, when it passes through air or water. How the direction changes affects what a person sees. What part of your eyes helps you see an image?

_____

_____

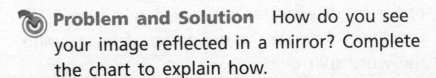 **Problem and Solution**   How do you see your image reflected in a mirror? Complete the chart to explain how.

Problem	Solution
You want to see your image in a mirror.	

PROBLEM AND SOLUTION

How do you see your image reflected in a mirror?

VOCABULARY

absorb To take in. *(verb)*

prism A transparent object that separates white light into all the colors of the rainbow. *(noun)*

VOCABULARY SKILL: Antonyms

Read the definition of the word *prism.* The word *separates* means "divides or splits." An opposite of *separates* is "unites" or "joins together." Rewrite the definition of *prism* using the word *split* or *divide.*

_____

_____

_____

2.c. Students know the color of light that hits an object affects the way the object is seen.

3 What Is Color?

Light hits an object. The color of the light affects the way you see the object.

The Colors of Sunlight

White light is made up of all the colors of the rainbow. Look at the picture. You can see many colors when light shines through the prism. A **prism** is a piece of glass or other transparent object. It is shaped like a triangle. It breaks white light into many colors.

A prism separates white light into colors.

Raindrops act like tiny prisms to create a rainbow.

Sunlight has many colors, too. When it is raining, you might see a rainbow if there is also some sunlight. That is because raindrops act like prisms. They break white light into colors. This makes a rainbow.

1. Complete the sentences to describe a prism.

    a. It is made of glass or other

    _____ material.

    b. It is shaped like a/an _____.

    c. It breaks white light into many

    _____.

I Wonder . . . One rainy day, the Sun began to shine through a break in the clouds. A rainbow appeared in the sky. Why did that happen? What do you think?

_____

_____

_____

_____

2. (Circle) the correct answer. When you are looking at a colored object, what do you see?

the light waves that are absorbed

the light waves that are reflected

the light waves that are refracted

3. Label the shoe to tell the color it will look when the light is turned on.

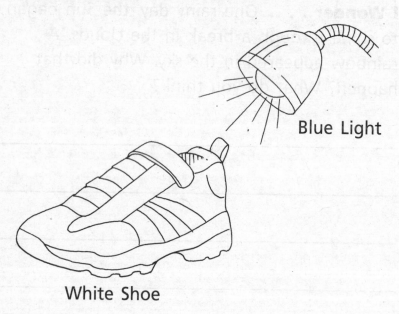

Blue Light

White Shoe

Seeing Colors

Light shines on an object. The object will **absorb** (uhb SAWRB), or take in, some of the light waves.

The object absorbs some colors. It reflects other colors. You see the reflected colors. You do not see the absorbed colors.

Bananas look yellow because they reflect yellow light. They absorb other colors.

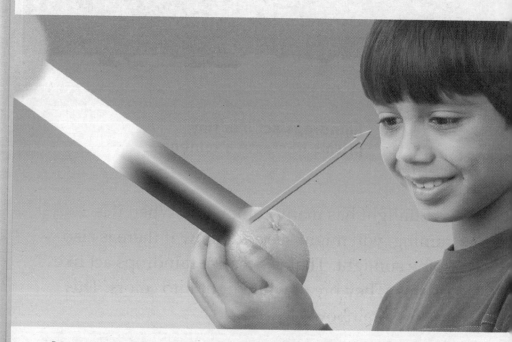

An orange absorbs all colors other than orange. So orange is the only color we see when we look at it.

Colored Light

The color of an object is based on the light it reflects. It is also based on the color of light shining on it.

White light is made up of all the colors of the rainbow. White objects reflect all of these colors, so they look white.

Shine a white light on a white shoe. It will look white. Shine a red light on the white shoe. It will look red.

red light

blue light

Shine a colored light on a white shoe and the shoe seems to change color.

SEQUENCE

How could you cause a white golf ball to appear blue, then red, then yellow?

Summary   White light is made up of all the colors of the rainbow. When white light strikes a colored object, the object absorbs some colors. It reflects other colors. You see only the reflected color. The color of the reflected light is the color of the object. The color of the light shining on an object also affects the way the object is seen. Complete the chart to explain why an apple looks red.

Light shines on a red apple.

↓

The apple _____ most colors of light.

↓

The apple _____ red light.

↓

You see a red apple.

Sequence   How could you cause a white golf ball to appear blue, then red, and then yellow?

_____

_____

Find the word *shadow*. Draw a picture showing how a shadow forms.

---

absorb (uhb SAWRB) To take in.

   absorber Tomar.

lens (lehnz) An object that refracts light.

   lente Objeto que refracta la luz.

light (lyt) A form of energy that you can see.

   luz Forma de energía que se puede ver.

opaque (OH payk) Not allowing light to pass through.

   opaco Que no permite que pase la luz.

prism (prihzm) A transparent object that separates white light into all the colors of the rainbow.

   prisma Objeto transparente que separa la luz blanca en todos los colores del arco iris.

Glossary

reflect (rih FLEHKT) To bounce off.

   reflejar Rebotar.

refract (rih FRAKT) To bend.

   refractar Cambiar de dirección.

shadow (sha DOH) An area where light does not strike the ground.

   sombra Zona donde la luz no llega al suelo.

translucent (trans LU sehnt) Allows only some light to pass through.

   traslúcido Que permite pasar sólo parte de la luz.

transparent (trans PAYR uhnt) Lets light pass through.

   transparente Que deja pasar la luz.

 Visit www.eduplace.com to play puzzles and word games.

Circle the English words and their meanings for all the glossary words.

Chapter Review

WHAT DID YOU LEARN?

Vocabulary

❶ (Circle) the correct answer.

Comprehension

❷ _____

❸ _____

❹ _____

   _____

Critical Thinking

❺ _____

   _____

   _____

   _____

Responding

Think About What You Have Read

Vocabulary

❶ A form of energy that you can see is _____.

   A) light

   B) lens

   C) prism

   D) shadow

Comprehension

❷ How do you see objects?

❸ What is the difference between *reflect* and *refract*?

❹ What happens to sunlight after it strikes a banana?

Critical Thinking

❺ A toy bear is on a dresser in front of a mirror. Why does the mirror produce a reflection, but the bear does not?

A

Absorb, 196, 198–199
Adaptations
  to changes in environment, 31
  for desert life, 8, 10, 12
  for forest life, 4–5, 7
  kinds of, 7, 9, 10, 12
  for life in aquatic habitats, 13–17
  for life in grasslands, 6, 7
  for life in the tundra, 8–9, 12
Air, 25, 75, 118
Ancestors, 53–57
Animals
  changing environments, 35
  of the desert, 10
  extinct and endangered, 45–48, 53–57
  fire and, 30–31
  floods and droughts and, 32–33
  of forests, 5
  of grasslands, 6
  needs of, 25–26, 28

  in the oceans, 15–16
  of tide pools, 13–14
  of the tundra, 9
  ways to stay safe, 12
  of wetlands, 17
Aquatic habitats
  oceans, 15–16
  tide pools, 13–14
  wetlands, 17
Atoms, 118, 120–121
  in compounds, 150, 152
  of elements, 146–147, 152
  periodic table of, 146, 148–149
Axis, 90, 91
  of the Moon, 99
  tilt of, 94–98

B

Batteries, 168
Behavior, 4, 7, 9, 10
Big Dipper, 107
Big Dog, 110
Biome, 4

Biomes
  aquatic habitats, 13–17
  deserts, 8, 10–11, 12
  forests, 4–5
  grasslands, 6
  tundra, 8–9, 12
Birds, 57
Bison, 46
Body parts, 7, 9, 10, 15
Brain, 179
Burning, 154, 156, 157

C

Charged particles, 176
Chemical change, 153–159
Chemical energy, 167, 168, 169, 171
Chemical property, 153, 154
Chemical reactions, 153–159
Color, 196–199
Community, 24
Competition, 24
Compounds, 146, 150–151, 152
Condensation, 138

Constellations, 106, 108–110
Cooking, 158
Craters, 70, 105
Crescent moon, 99, 102
Crest of a wave, 173

D

Dating fossils, 52
Day
  on Earth, 90–93, 98
  on planets, 72, 73, 74, 75, 76,
    79, 80, 81
Desert, 8, 10, 12
Dinosaurs, 44–45, 57
Dodo bird, 47
Drought, 32
Dwarf planet, 71, 83

E

Earth
  day and night cycle, 90–93, 98
  information from fossils about,
    49–52
  Moon of, 69, 99–105
  orbit of, 90–91

as a planet, 69, 70, 75
  revolution of, 94–98, 110
  rotation of, 90–93, 109
  seasons of, 94–98
Ecosystem, 24, 25
Electrical charge, 176
Electrical energy, 167, 171,
  176–179
Electric circuits, 176, 177, 178
Electric current, 176, 178
Elements, 146–147, 152
  compounds of, 150–151, 152
  periodic table of, 146, 148–149
Elephants, 53–54
Emu, 55
Endangered species, 44, 46, 48
Energy
  changing forms of, 171, 178
  conversion from potential to
    kinetic, 169–170
  forms of, 166–168, 176–179
  of friction, 172
  movement through waves,
    173–175
  storing and releasing, 169
  thermal energy, 131–138
Environment, 8–9

changes in, 24, 26–29, 30–37
  desert, 8, 10–11, 12
  extinction and, 45
  forests, 4–5, 7
  grasslands, 6–7
  oceans, 15–16
  tide pools, 13–14
  tundra, 8–9, 12
  wetlands, 17
Equator, 94, 95
Era, 49, 52
Evaporation, 136–137
Exploding, 154
Extinct species, 44–47, 53–57
Eye, 195

F

Fall, 94–95
Fire, 30–31, 45
Flood, 32
Food, 25, 158, 168, 171
Forces, 172
Forest fire, 30–31
Forest friends, 4
Forests, 7
Forms of matter, 124–131

Fossils, 49–52
Freezing, 138
Friction, 169
Full moon, 99, 101, 103

G

Gases, 124–125, 130–131
  evaporation and, 136–137
  of planets, 70, 71, 79
  sound waves moving through,
    175
  in stars, 106
Gas giants, 79–82
  Jupiter, 71, 79
  Neptune, 71, 79, 82
  Saturn, 70, 80
  Uranus, 71, 79, 81
Grassland, 4, 6, 7
Great Red Spot, 79

H

Habitats, 4
  desert, 8, 10–11, 12
  forests, 4–5, 7
  grasslands, 6

oceans, 15–16
tide pools, 13–14
tundra, 8–9, 12
wetlands, 17
Hand lens, 194
Heart, 179
Heat, 131
Hemispheres, 95
Hubble Space Telescope, 67
Human body
  electricity and, 179

I

Imprint fossils, 49
Inner planets, 68, 70
  Earth, 75
  exploring, 77–78
  Mars, 76
  Mercury, 70, 73
  Venus, 70, 74

J

Jupiter, 71, 79

K

Kinetic energy, 169

L

Landslides, 173
Laws, 37
Legs, 7
Lens, 192, 194–195
Light energy, 167, 171, 178
Light waves, 15, 107, 187–191
  absorption of, 198–199
  color and, 196–199
  opaque objects and, 189
  reflected, 192, 198–199
  refracted, 192, 193
  shadows and, 190–191
  sight and, 187, 199
  from the Sun, 90–104
  translucent objects and, 189
  transparent objects and, 188
Liquid, 124–125, 128–129, 131
  evaporation of, 136–137
  melting and, 134–135
  sound waves moving through,
    175

Living things
  adaptations of, 4–17
  changing environments, 34–37
  communities and populations
    of, 24
  competition among, 26–29
  of the desert, 8, 10–11
  on Earth only, 70, 75
  endangered, 44–48
  extinct, 45–48
  of forests, 4–5, 7
  fossils of, 49–52
  of grasslands, 6
  needs of, 25–27, 107
  of oceans, 15–16
  of tide pools, 13–14
  of the tundra, 8–9
  ways to stay safe, 12
  of wetlands, 17

M

Magnify, 64
Mars, 70, 76
Mass, 118
Matter, 118

adding and taking away heat,
    132–138
atoms of, 120–121
chemical changes, 153–159
compounds of, 150–151, 152
condensation, 138
elements of, 146–147, 152
energy and, 166
evaporation, 136–137
forms of, 124–131
freezing, 138
melting, 134–135
mixture of, 152
periodic table of elements,
    148–149
physical changes, 122–123,
    134–138
properties of, 118, 149,
    150–151, 152
sound waves moving through,
    175
Mechanical energy, 167, 171
Melting, 134–135
Mercury, 70, 72
Mirrors, 192
Mixture, 152

Moon, 64, 69, 75
  phases of, 99–104
  revolution of, 100
  rotation of, 99, 100
  surface of, 105
Moons of other planets, 68, 69,
    73, 74, 76, 79, 80, 81, 82, 83
Motion, 169, 170

N

Neptune, 71, 79, 82
New moon, 101, 102, 104
Night, 90–93, 106–110
Nonliving things, 8, 30–33
Northern Hemisphere, 95, 97

O

Oceans, 15–16
Opaque objects, 189
Optical telescopes, 66
Orbit, 68, 72, 73, 75, 83, 90–91
Organisms. See Living things
Outer planets, 68, 71
  Jupiter, 71, 79
  Neptune, 71, 79, 82

Saturn, 71, 79, 80
Uranus, 71, 79, 81

P

Paleontologist, 49, 50, 52
Particles
  condensation and, 138
  evaporation and, 136–137
  freezing and, 138
  of gases, 130, 131
  of liquids, 129, 131
  melting and, 134–135
  of solids, 127, 131
People
  changing environments, 34,
    36–37
  as threat to species, 28, 46–47
Periodic table, 146, 148–149
Phases of the Moon, 100–104
Physical change, 118, 122–123,
    153, 155–156
  condensation, 138
  evaporation, 136–137
  freezing, 138
  melting, 134–135

Physical properties, 118, 124,
    126–127
Planets, 64, 68, 69
  Earth, 70, 75
  inner planets, 70, 73–78
  Jupiter, 71, 79
  Mars, 76
  Mercury, 70, 73
  Neptune, 71, 79, 82
  orbits of, 72
  outer planets, 71, 79–82
  Pluto, 83
  Saturn, 71, 79, 80
  Uranus, 71, 79, 81
  Venus, 70, 74
Plants
  changes to environment by, 34
  changing environments, 34
  of the desert, 11, 12
  fire and, 30–31
  floods and droughts and,
    32–33
  of forests, 4
  of grasslands, 6
  needs of, 25–27
  in the oceans, 15
  stems of, 11

  of tide pools, 13
  of the tundra, 9
  ways to stay safe, 12
  of wetlands, 17
Pluto, 71, 83
Pollution, 36–37
Population, 24, 29
Position, 169–170
Potential energy, 169
Prism, 196–197
Properties
  chemical changes and, 154–159
  chemical property, 153
  of compounds, 150–151, 152
  of elements, 149
  of gases, 130–131
  of liquids, 128–129, 131
  of mixtures, 152
  physical, 118
  of solids, 126–127, 131
  of waves, 173

Q

Quarter moon, 99, 101, 102,
    103, 104

R

Radio telescopes, 66
Rain, 6, 10, 197
Reflection, 192
Refraction, 192, 193–194
Relatives, 53–56
Reproduction, 24, 27
Resources, 24, 25–26, 29
Revolution, 94–98, 99, 100–104
Rhinoceros, 56
Rings, 80
Rotation, 90–91, 99
Rover, 78
Rusting, 154

S

Saturn, 71, 79, 80
Scorpius, 110
Seasons, 94–98
Sea turtles, 45
Senses, 118
Shadows, 93, 190–191
Sight, 187, 195, 198–199
Sirius, 110
Solar system, 68–69

Earth, 90–93, 109, 110
inner planets, 70, 73–78
Moon of Earth, 99–105
orbits, 72
outer planets, 79–82
planets, 68–82
Pluto, 71, 83
Sun, 68, 90–93, 107
Solids, 124–127, 131
melting of, 134–135
sound waves moving through, 175
Sound energy, 167, 174–175, 178
Sound waves, 174–175
Space probe, 73, 77–78
Space to live, 25, 27
Species, 44–48
Spring, 94–95
Stars, 64, 106–110
constellations, 108–110
position in the sky, 109–110
Sun as, 68, 107
Stems, 11
Structural adaptations, 7, 9, 10, 11, 15
Summer, 94–95

Sun
daylight hours and, 98
light from, 69
phases of the Moon and, 99–104
place in the sky, 90–93, 96–97
planets and, 68
seasons and, 94–98
as a star, 64, 107
Switch, 178

T

Telescopes, 64–67, 77
Thermal energy, 131–138, 167, 171
condensing and, 138
evaporation and, 136–137
freezing and, 138
melting and, 134–135
Tide pools, 13
Tools
hand lens, 194
space probe, 77–78
telescopes, 64
Traits, 53, 54–57
Translucent objects, 189

Transparent objects, 188
Trees, 4, 8
Trough of a wave, 173
Tsunami, 45
Tundra, 8–9, 12

U

Uranus, 71, 79, 81

V

Venus, 70, 74
Vibration, 174
Volcanoes, 45

W

Waning moon, 99, 101, 103, 104
Water, 13–14, 15, 25
Water habitats, 12–17
Wavelength, 173
Waves, 173–175
Waxing moon, 99, 101, 102, 104
Wetlands, 17

White light, 196, 199
Winter, 94–95

Y

Year, 72, 74, 75, 76, 82, 94